Grade 1

Home-School Connection

McGraw Hill Macmillan McGraw-Hill

Credits: pages 489, 490

The *McGraw-Hill* Companies

Macmillan
McGraw-Hill

Published by Macmillan/McGraw-Hill, of McGraw-Hill Education, a division of The McGraw-Hill
Companies, Inc., Two Penn Plaza, New York, New York 10121-2298.

Printed in the United States of America

4 5 6 7 8 9 045 10 09 08 07

Contents

Beginning of the Year Letter
in English and Spanish

▲ Decodable Readers   ● On-Level Books

▲ Decodable Readers   ● On-Level Books

Dear Family Member:

You can help your child practice reading skills taught at school. Working together you and your child can become partners in learning.

Each week your child will bring home:

- A **letter** that tells you about the book the class is reading that week

- Three **homework activities** that will improve reading skills and offer practice with words your child is learning

- One or two **stories** for the two of you to read together

Your interest, praise, and encouragement are sure to lead to your child's success.

Queridos familiares:

Con su ayuda, su niño/a puede practicar las destrezas de lectura aprendidas en la escuela. Este trabajo conjunto les permitirá ser compañeros de aprendizaje.

Cada semana, su niño/a va a llevar a casa lo siguiente:

- Una **carta** contándole acerca lo que ha leído en clase durante esa semana.

- Tres **actividades de tareas para el hogar** para mejorar las destrezas de lectura y practicar las palabras que está aprendiendo.

- También llevará a casa uno o dos **cuentos** para leer juntos.

Su interés, apoyo y estímulo guiarán a su niño/a al éxito.

Home-School Connection

Dear Family M

I'm reading Po week. I'm learnin in the story from act and what the characters in this are Pam and Sam rabbit, and her fr a bird. The story the friends playir Some things Pam and Sam cannot. Sam can do some things that Pam cannot do!

This Week's Sl

Comprehension: character and setting

Phonics: the sound of *a* as in *bat*

Spelling: words with *a*

Name _____

···········(fold here)·········

© Macmillan/McGraw-Hill

Word Workout

WORDS TO KNOW

jump   up   down   not

Tell Me Can you tell me what these words mean? Then we can make up a sentence using each word.

MY SPELLING WORDS

can   cat   hat

man   mat   ran

Rhyme Time I'm going to ask you to spell each word. Tell me which words rhyme with *can*. Which words rhyme with *mat*?

7

Meet Cat

Let's get to know Cat. We can talk about every picture and decide what kind of animal Cat is. Is she friendly? Is she helpful? What is she like? What does she do?

Cat sees her neighbor Mr. Pig. She helps him with his bags.

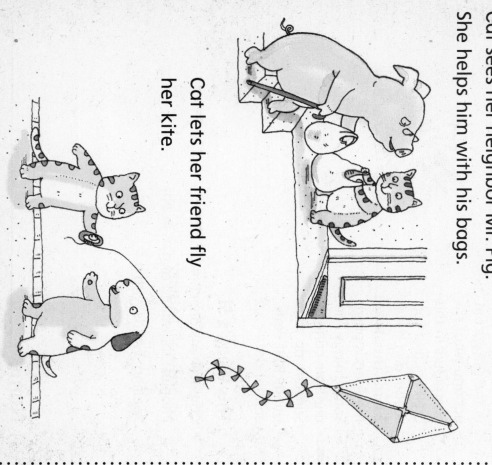

Cat lets her friend fly her kite.

Cat tells her family a funny story. She makes her family laugh!

Cat sees that Birdy cannot fly. She fixes Birdy's leg.

Cat takes the trash out for her dad.

8

Queridos familiares:

Estoy leyendo *Pam and Sam* en la clase esta semana. Estoy aprendiendo sobre los personajes del cuento por cómo se comportan y por lo que dicen. Los personajes en este cuento son Pam y Sam. Pam es una coneja y su amigo Sam es un pájaro. El cuento comienza con los amigos jugando. Hay cosas que Pam puede hacer y que Sam no puede hacer. ¡Y Sam puede hacer cosas que Pam no puede hacer!

Destrezas de la semana

Comprensión: personajes y ambiente

Fonética: el sonida de la a como en *bat*

Ortografía: palabras con a

(fold here)

© Macmillan/McGraw-Hill

Nombre _____

Ejercicio de palabras

PALABRAS DE VOCABULARIO

jump   up   down   not

Dime ¿Puedes decirme las definiciones de estas palabras? Luego vamos a escribir una oración usando cada palabra.

PALABRAS DE ORTOGRAFÍA

can	cat	hat
man	mat	ran

Vamos a rimar Te voy a pedir que escribas cada palabra. Dime qué palabras riman con la palabra *can*. ¿Qué palabras riman con la palabra *mat*?

Conoce a Gata

Vamos a conocer a Gata. Vamos a hablar acerca de cada dibujo y decidir qué clase de animal es Gata. ¿Es amistosa? ¿Le gusta ayudar? ¿Cómo es ella? ¿Qué es lo que hace?

Cat sees her neighbor Mr. Pig. She helps him with his bags.

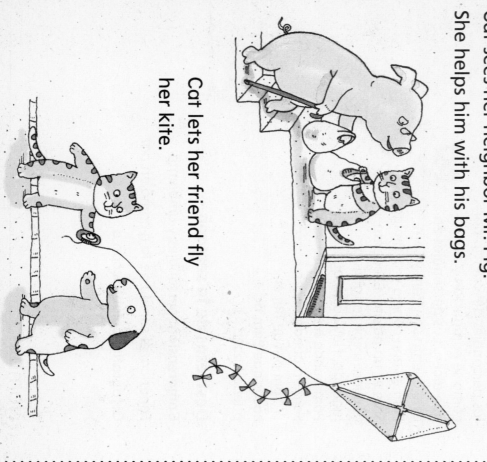

Cat lets her friend fly her kite.

Cat tells her family a funny story. She makes her family laugh!

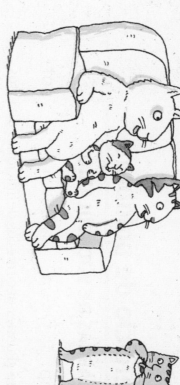

Cat sees that Birdy cannot fly. She fixes Birdy's leg.

Cat takes the trash out for her dad.

A Cap for Pam

by Kathryn Lewis
illustrated by Chi Chung

This page is intentionally blank.

Sam has a tan mat.

2

This page is intentionally blank.

A Cap for Pam

Can Pam have a mat?

3

Pam Cat can tap!
Tap, Pam, tap!

6

Sam has a cat cap.
Pam can have a cap!

4

A Cap for Pam

© 2007 Macmillan/McGraw-Hill

Pam ran with the cap.

5

Can You?

by Paul Dan

illustrated by Jill Newton

Comprehension Check

Retell the Story

Use a Character Chart to help you retell about Little Bat and Frog.

Think and Compare

1. What can Little Bat do that is special?

2. What can you do that is special?

3. Name an animal. Tell what is special about it.

8

"I can jump," said Frog.
"I can jump up
and down."

2

Can You?

"I can fly!" said Little Bat.

7

"I can jump," said Rabbit.
"I can jump up
and down."

3

"I can not jump,"
said Little Bat.
"I can not jump up.
I can not jump down."

6

"I can jump, too!" said Kangaroo.

4

"I can jump up and down."

5

Dear Family Member:

I'm reading *I Can! Can You?* in class this week. I learned that events in a story happen in a certain order. This story begins with a little girl jumping in the air with her hands on her hat. Her friend follows her and shows that he can do the same thing. I wonder if they will keep following each other?

This Week's Skills

Comprehension: sequence

Phonics: the sound of a as in *mad*

Spelling: words with a

.... (fold here) ....

© Macmillan/McGraw-Hill

Name _____

Word Workout

WORDS TO KNOW

over   it   yes   too

Make a Sentence Let's read the words together. Then, I will say a sentence for each word, using "blank" instead of the word. You can repeat the sentence and add the missing word.

SPELLING WORDS

dad   sack   sad

Art Time Draw a picture for each word. Then write the word for each picture.

Jack's Day

Put your pencil on **Go**. I'll read aloud what Jack does on Saturday. Draw a line to follow where Jack goes. Go in order until you get to Stop.

First, Jack plays soccer.

Next, he gets popcorn.

Then he goes to the library.

Last, he gets a haircut.

Now it is time to go home.

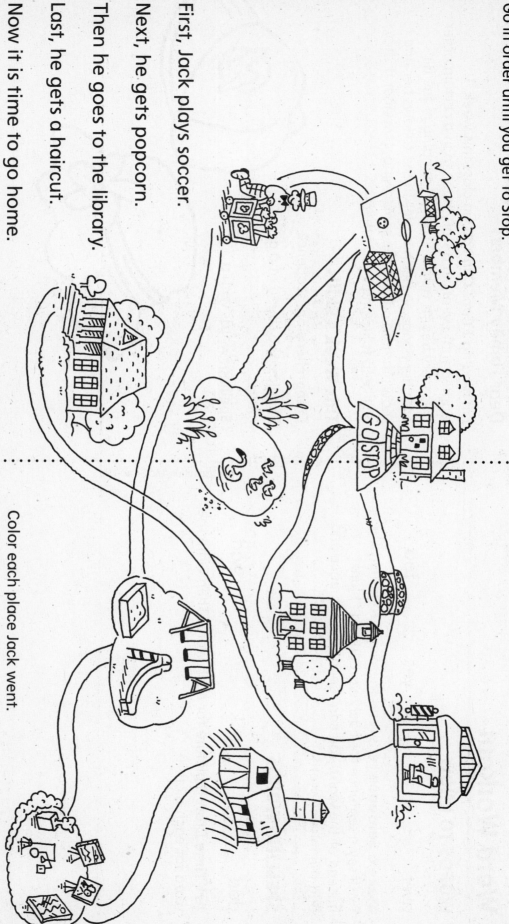

Color each place Jack went.

Queridos familiares:

Estoy leyendo *I Can! Can You?* en la clase esta semana. Aprendí que los sucesos ocurren en un cierto orden. Este cuento comienza con una pequeña niña que salta en el aire con sus manos sobre su sombrero. Su amigo la copia y demuestra que puede hacer lo mismo. ¿Me pregunto si ellos seguirán copiándose el uno al otro?

Destrezas de la semana

Comprensión: orden de los sucesos

Fonética: el sonido de *a* como en *mad*

Ortografía: palabras con *a*

Nombre _____

© Macmillan/McGraw-Hill

Ejercicio de palabras

PALABRAS DE VOCABULARIO

over   it   yes   too

Hacer una oración Leamos juntos las palabras. Luego, voy a decir una oración para cada palabra usando la palabra blank en lugar de la palabra que debe ir. Puedes repetir la oración y añade la palabra que falta.

PALABRAS DE ORTOGRAFÍA

dad   sack   sad

Vamos a dibujar Haz un dibujo para cada palabra. Luego escribe la palabra para cada dibujo.

El día de Jack

Coloca tu lápiz en la palabra *Go*. Voy a leer en voz alta lo que Jack hace los sábados. Traza una línea para seguir adónde va Jack. Sigue el orden hasta que llegues a la palabra *Stop*.

First, Jack plays soccer.

Next, he gets popcorn.

Then he goes to the library.

Last, he has a haircut.

Now it is time to go home.

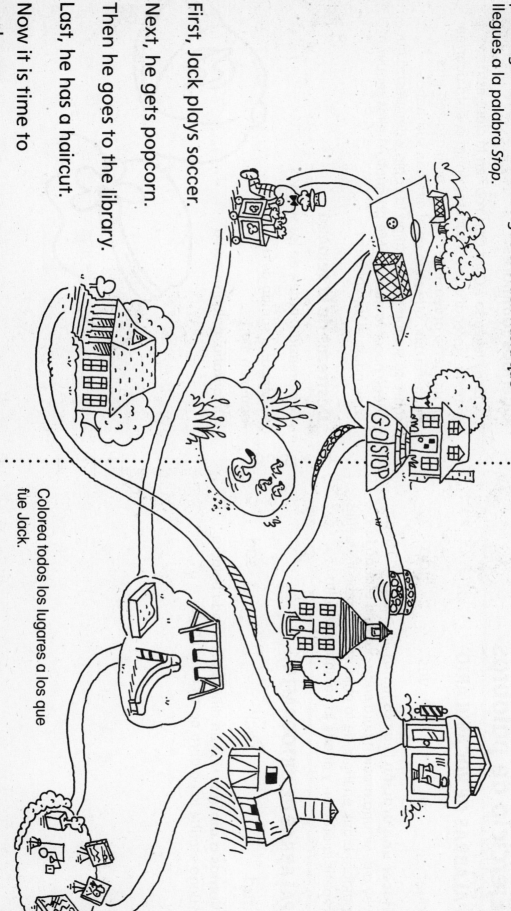

Colorea todos los lugares a los que fue Jack.

22

I Can, I Can!

by Carol Lindeen

This page is intentionally blank.

8

I can jump up and down.

I Can, I Can!

This page is intentionally blank.

I can swing a fat bat.

I Can, I Can!

I have a tan mat.
I can nap, nap, nap.

I am not little.
I can carry a back pack.

I Can, I Can!

Hal can tag Val.
I can tag Hal.

We Like Sports

by Steve Jones

Comprehension Check

Retell

Use a Sequence Chart to help you retell which sports you read about.

First

▼

Next

▼

Last

Think and Compare

1. What sport did you read about first? What sport did you read about next?

2. Which sport do you like best?

3. Name two team sports.

8

Is it fun to play tennis?

Yes! You can hit a ball.

7

Yes! You can hit a ball
over the net!

3

Is it fun to play golf, too?

6

4

Is it fun to play soccer?

We Like Sports

© 2007 Macmillan/McGraw-Hill

Yes! You can kick a ball.

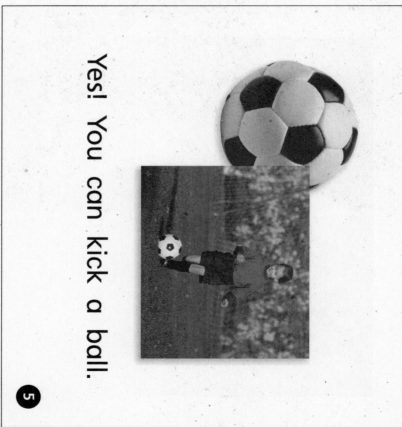

5

Dear Family Member:

I'm reading How You Grew in class this week. I learned that things in a story happen in order. This is called sequence. How You Grew begins by telling us things we could do when we were babies. It keeps showing us things we can do when we get older and older. I wonder what I will do when I get older!

This Week's Skills

Comprehension: sequence

Phonics: the sound of *i* as in *bit*

Spelling: words with i

(fold here)

© Macmillan/McGraw-Hill

Name _____

Word Workout

WORDS TO KNOW

run   ride   be

Lots of Sentences Let's see how many different sentences we can make for each word.

MY SPELLING WORDS

hit   kiss   miss

pin   sit   win

Sounds Right? Spell each word as I say it. Tell me what letter is in every word. Does that letter stand for the same sound in each word? Tell me other letters and how many words they are in.

Where Does the Time Go?

A time line shows events in the order in which they happen. Let's talk about the things you could do at the different ages shown here.

1 day old

1 day old
I was born
_____ .

1 year old
When I was one year old, I could
_____
_____ .

1 year old

4 years old

7 years old

4 years old
When I was four years old, I could
_____
_____ .

7 years old
Now I can
_____
_____ .

Queridos familiares:

Estoy leyendo *How You Grew* en clase esta semana. Aprendí que las cosas en un cuento suceden en orden. A esto se le llama *orden de los sucesos*. El cuento *How You Grew* comienza contándonos las cosas que podíamos hacer cuando éramos bebés. Luego nos sigue mostrando cosas que podemos hacer a medida que crecemos más y más. ¡Me pregunto qué haré cuando sea grande!

Destrezas de la semana

Comprensión: orden de sucesos

Fonética: el sonido de la i como en *bit*

Ortografía: palabras con i

Nombre _____

(Fold here)

© Macmillan/McGraw-Hill

Ejercicio de palabras

PALABRAS DE VOCABULARIO

run   ride   be

Muchas oraciones Veamos cuántas oraciones diferentes podemos hacer con cada palabra.

PALABRAS DE ORTOGRAFÍA

hit   kiss   miss

pin   sit   win

¿Suena bien? Deletrea cada palabra cuando la digo. Dime qué letra hay en todos las palabras. ¿Representa esa letra el mismo sonido en cada palabra? Dime otras letras y cuántas palabras tienen esas letras.

33

¿Adónde se va el tiempo?

Una línea cronológica muestra los sucesos en el orden que ocurren. Hablemos acerca de las cosas que puedes hacer a las diferentes edades que aparecen a continuación.

I day old •——————————• I year old

4 years old •——————————• 7 years old

I day old
I was born
_____
_____ .

I year old
When I was one year old, I could
_____
_____ .

4 years old
When I was four years old I could
_____
_____ .

7 years old
Now I can
_____
_____ .

Jim Had a Big Hit!

by Liz Rivera

illustrated by Kathryn Mitter

This page is intentionally blank.

14

"Can I hit, too?"
said Jim to Zack.

Jim Had a Big Hit!

This page is intentionally blank.

Jim Had a Big Hit!

Jim was at bat.
Jim sat back as he hit!

"I hit it over!" said Jim.
"Yip! Yip! Yip!" said Wag.

Jim had a big, big, big rip.
Can Dad fix it? Yes!

16

Jim Had a Big Hit!   © 2007 Macmillan/McGraw-Hill

Jim had his bat back.
Jim did not quit!

17

We Grow Up

by Jan Dree

Comprehension Check

Retell

Look back at the pictures in this book. Use them to talk to a partner about growing up.

Think and Compare

1. What does a baby do before she can walk?

2. What things do you like to do?

3. What things will you do when you are a grownup?

16

2

This little baby is 1.

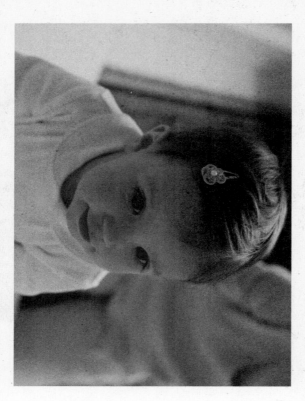

We Grow Up

© 2007 Macmillan/McGraw-Hill

She can ride
a horse.

15

She can crawl.

We Grow Up

This girl is 14. What can she do?

4

This little boy is 2.

He can ride his bike fast.

13

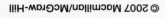

He can walk.

This boy will be 12.
What can he do?

This little girl will be 3.

She can ride the bus to school.

She can run.

7

This girl will be 6.
What can she do?

10

This boy is 4.

We Grow Up

He can jump.

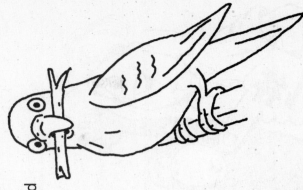

Dear Family Member:

I'm reading *Pet Tricks* in class this week. I learned that every story has a setting. A setting tells where and when a story takes place. This story takes place at a pet show where all the pets do tricks. A puppy named Frizz can jump over a bat. I wonder if a lizard and a kitten can do interesting tricks, too!

This Week's Skills

Comprehension: character and setting

Phonics: the sounds of **br, fr, cr, gr,** and **tr**

Spelling: words beginning with **cr-, gr-,** and **tr-**

(fold here)

Name _____

Word Workout

WORDS TO KNOW

come	that	on	good

Tell Me Tell me a story about a pet named Gina. What kind of pet is she? How does she act? You can use these words for your story.

MY SPELLING WORDS

crab	crib	grass	trap	trip
grab				

Add a Word Let's fold a piece of lined paper into three columns. Write **cr, gr,** and **tr** at the top of the columns. Write your new spelling words in the right columns. Let's think of other words we could add to the list.

Where Is Champ?

We can read and talk about where Champ the chimp is. You can draw a picture to show what each place looks like.

Champ is at a baseball game.

Champ is at the toy store.

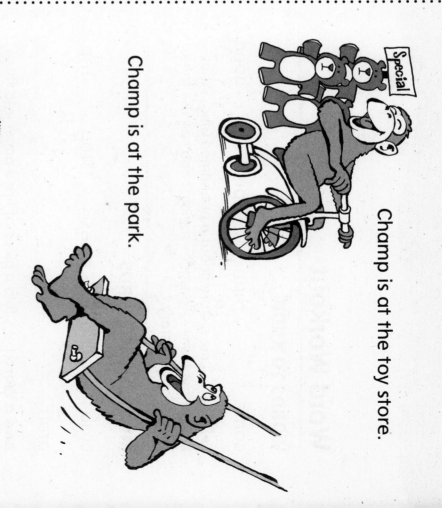

Champ is at the park.

Champ is in his room.

Queridos familiares:

Estoy leyendo *Pet Tricks* en la clase esta semana. Aprendí que cada cuento ocurre en un lugar, o ambiente. Un ambiente nos dice dónde y cuándo ocurre el cuento. Este cuento ocurre en un espectáculo de mascotas en donde todas las mascotas hacen trucos. Un cachorro llamado Frizz puede saltar por encima de un bate. ¡Me pregunto si una lagartija y un gatito pueden hacer trucos interesantes también!

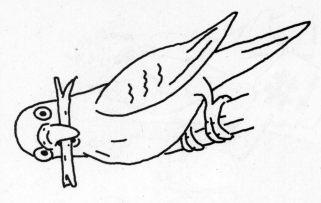

Destrezas de la semana

Comprensión: personajes y ambiente

Fonética: los sonidos de **br, fr, cr, gr y tr**

Ortografía: palabras que comienzan con **cr, gr y tr**

Nombre _____

·········(fold here)·········

© Macmillan/McGraw-Hill

Ejercicio de palabras

PALABRAS DE VOCABULARIO

come   that   on   good

Dime Dime un cuento sobre un animal doméstico que se llama Gina. ¿Qué tipo de animal doméstico es? ¿Cómo se comporta? Puedes usar estas palabras para tu cuento.

PALABRAS DE ORTOGRAFÍA

crab   crib   grass   trap   trip

grab

Agregar una palabra Doblemos una hoja de papel con renglones en tres partes para formar tres columnas. Escribe **cr, gr y tr** en la parte superior de las columnas. Escribe tus palabras nuevas de ortografía en la columna correcta. Pensemos en otras palabras que podemos agregar a la lista.

¿Dónde está Champ?

Vamos a leer y a hablar acerca de dónde se encuentra Champ, el chimpancé. Puedes hacer un dibujo para mostrar cómo es cada lugar.

Champ is at a baseball game.

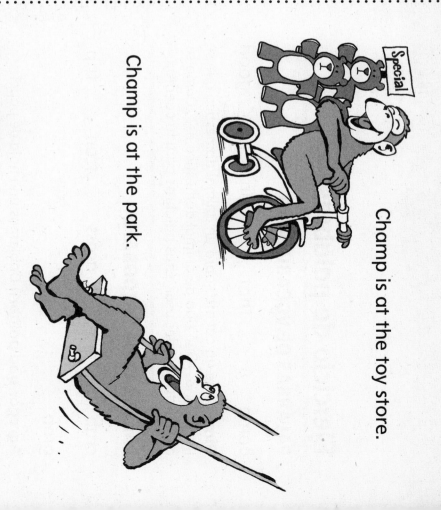

Champ is at the toy store.

Champ is at the park.

Champ is in his room.

Grab a Crab

by Mindy Menschell

This page is intentionally blank.

A crab can be big.
I can grab it.

20

This page is intentionally blank.

This cat can run.
I can grab it.

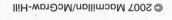

Grab a Crab

It can sit.
It can do tricks!

It sits in the grass.
I can grin at it.

22

It can run.
I can ride it.

23

Rosa's New Puppy

by Julia Diago

illustrated by John Wallace

Comprehension Check

Retell the Story

Use a Setting Chart to help you tell where the characters are and what they do.

Setting	What the Characters Do There

Think and Compare

1. Where does Rosa's puppy go to eat?

2. What would you do with the puppy if it were yours?

3. What other animals are good pets?

16

Rosa got a new puppy.

Rosa's New Puppy

© 2007 Macmillan/McGraw-Hill

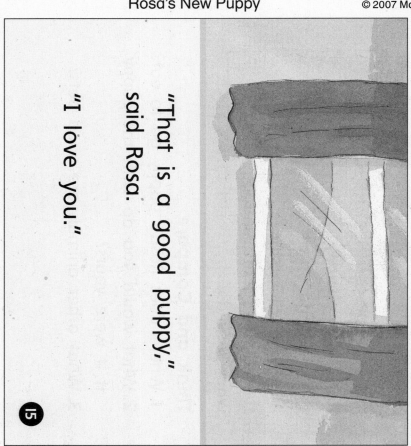

"That is a good puppy,"
said Rosa.

"I love you."

"That is a good puppy,"
said Rosa.

3

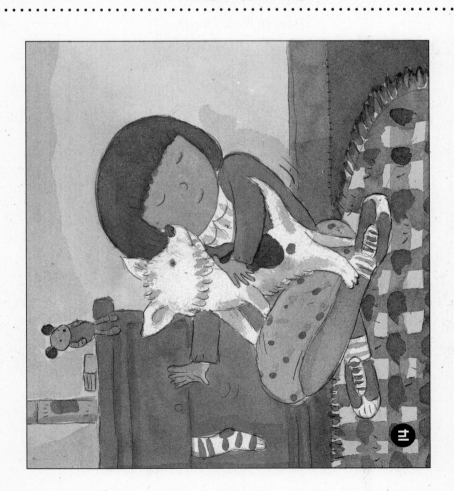

4

Rosa's New Puppy

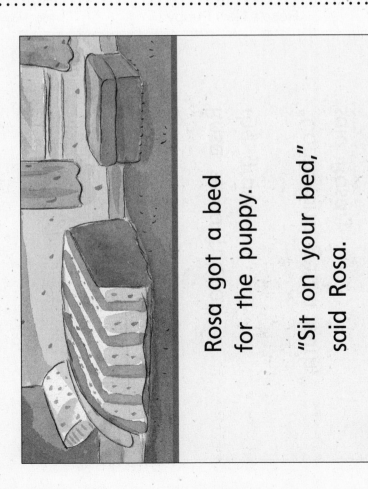

Rosa set a bowl
on the floor.

"Come and drink,"
said Rosa.

5

Rosa got a bed
for the puppy.

"Sit on your bed,"
said Rosa.

12

9

Rosa set a dish
on the floor.

Rosa's New Puppy

© 2007 Macmillan/McGraw-Hill

Rosa set a tub on
the grass.

"Come and get a bath,"
said Rosa.

11

"Come and eat,"
said Rosa.

Rosa's New Puppy

8

Rosa got a leash
for the puppy.

Rosa's New Puppy

9

"Come and walk,"
said Rosa.

Dear Family Member:

I'm reading *Soccer* in class this week. I learned that authors write to tell a story or to give us information. *Soccer* gives information about a sport. Soccer players run. They kick the ball. They cannot use their hands. Soccer takes a lot of teamwork.

This Week's Skills

Comprehension: author's purpose

Phonics: the sounds of **nd, nk, nt,** and **st**

Spelling: words that end in **nd, nk, nt,** and **st**

Name _____

(Fold here)

Word Workout

WORDS TO KNOW

help   now   use   very

Have a Ball Draw a picture of yourself playing a game. Use the new words in a sentence to describe your picture.

MY SPELLING WORDS

sand   sink   west

land   fast   sent

Write It Right Write each word in the air with your arm as you spell it. Then write each word on a piece of paper.

Story or Information?

I'll read aloud each book idea, and you can read along with me. Then tell me if the idea is telling a story or giving information. For the last item, draw your own picture to go along with the idea.

1. Apples can be used for drinks and desserts. You can make apple cider and apple pie.

Story or information?

2. The dog surprised everyone. He was playing the trumpet in the band!

Story or information?

3. School buses are very useful. They bring us to school and take us to field trips.

Story or information?

4. The rabbit and the turtle became best friends. The rabbit always made the turtle laugh.

Story or information?

Conexión con el hogar

Queridos familiares:

Estoy leyendo *Soccer* en la clase esta semana. Aprendí que los autores o autoras escriben para contar un cuento o para darnos información. El cuento *Soccer* ofrece información sobre un deporte. Los jugadores de fútbol corren y patean la pelota. No pueden usar sus manos. Para jugar fútbol es necesario un buen trabajo en equipo.

Destrezas de la semana

Comprensión: propósito del autor

Fonética: los sonidos de
nd, nk, nt y st

Ortografía: palabras
que terminen en
nd, nk, nt y st

Nombre _____

(fold here)

© Macmillan/McGraw-Hill

Ejercicio de palabras

PALABRAS DE VOCABULARIO

help   now   use   very

A divertirse Haz un dibujo de ti mismo jugando un juego. Usa las palabras nuevas en una oración para describir tu dibujo.

PALABRAS DE ORTOGRAFÍA

sand   sink   west

land   fast   sent

Escribir correctamente Escribe cada palabra en el aire con tu mano letra por letra. Luego escribe cada palabra en una hoja de papel.

65

Cuento del tres en raya

Cada uno de nosotros elije un color diferente de creyón y comienza a jugar.

- Lee a continuación la primera idea para un cuento.

- Si crees que es una idea para un cuento, escribe **S** donde quieras en un tablero del tres en raya.

- Si crees es una idea de un libro informativo, escribe **I** donde quieras.

- Vamos a tomar turnos. Gana el primero que tenga tres colores iguales alineados.

- A rabbit and bird are friends.

- How babies grow

- Dog that plays in a band

- Dogs that help blind people

- A girl's pet follows her to school.

- Things that are made from apples

- A boy helps on his family's farm.

- A girl wishes for a baby brother.

- Zach misses the school bus.

- Things that float or sink

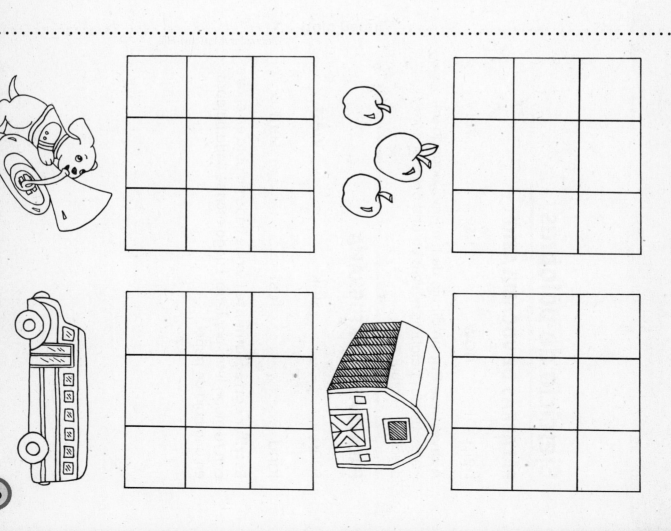

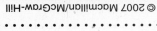

KIDS CAN DO IT FAST!

by Ming Chin Lee

Kids Can Do It Fast!

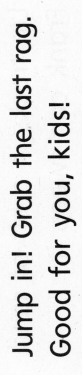

Jump in! Grab the last rag.
Good for you, kids!

32

Kids can fill that sack.
Kids can fill it fast.

Kids Can Do It Fast!

Lin tracks in a bit of sand.
Frank can sweep it.

Come on, kids!
You can lift big bags.

Kids Can Do It Fast!

It will land in the grass.
Pat and Dan can grab it.

30

Lil has a quick quiz.
Can Lil print a list?

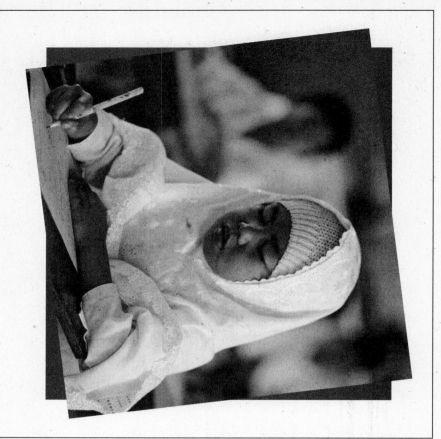

Kids Can Do It Fast!   © 2007 Macmillan/McGraw-Hill

Kim stands at the sink.
Kim hands Matt a dish.

We Can Help

by Bonnie Ferraro

Comprehension Check

Retell

Use an Author's Purpose Chart to help you retell why the author wrote this book.

Author's Purpose

Think and Compare

1. What did the author want you to know?
2. Tell about how you helped someone.
3. How can people keep beaches clean?

16

2

Look at the sand.
We can not use
the sand.

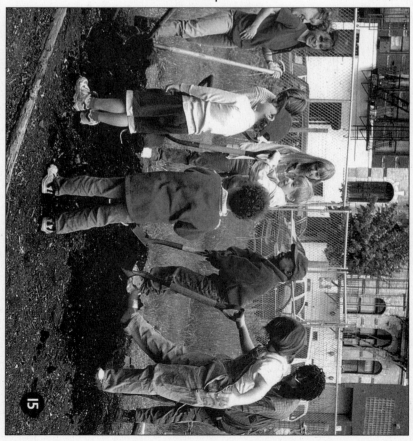

15

We Can Help

3

Look at the lot.
We can help!

4

We can help.
We can pick up.

4

We Can Help

13

We Can Help

5

Look! The park
is very clean.
We can use
the park now.

12

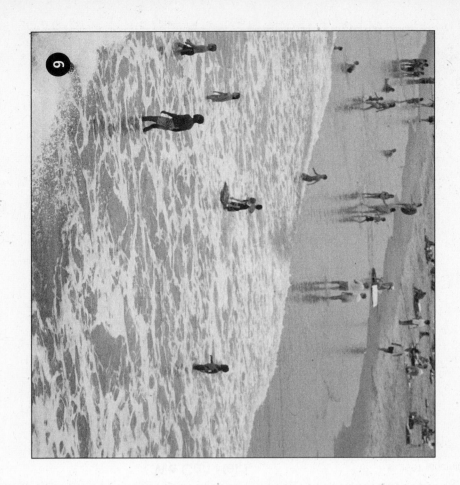

We Can Help

Look! The sand
is very clean.
We can use the sand now.

We can help!
We can pick up.

Look at the park.
We can not use the park.

8

9

Dear Family Member:

I'm reading *Animal Moms and Dads* in class this week. I learned that every selection has a main idea. The main idea is what the selection is mostly about. The details tell me more about the main idea. This selection tells how animal moms and dads care for their babies. Animal moms can bring their babies food. Animal dads can get the bugs out of their baby's fur coat! Animal moms and dads seem to take care of their babies like you take care of me!

This Week's Skills

Comprehension: main idea and details

Phonics: words with the sound of **o** as in *cot*

Spelling: words with **o**

Name _____

(fold here)

© Macmillan/McGraw-Hill

Word Workout

WORDS TO KNOW

one   two   they   her   does

Remember Think about the book you are reading this week. Let's use the words above to talk about animal parents and other family members.

MY SPELLING WORDS

hog   hot   log

top   hop   lot

Letter Take Away Repeat each word that I say. Spell the word. Take away the first letter of the word and say each word again. What does **o** sound like in each word? Can we find other words that have the same sound?

All About a Tiger

Below is a picture of a tiger. What do you think we're about to talk about? Write the main idea on the line. On the next page, circle the details that match the main idea. Use the pictures as clues.

Main Idea: _____

I.

a. It has whiskers.

b. It flies in the sky.

2.

a. It lives in the ocean.

b. It has a loud roar.

3.

a. It doesn't have a tail.

b. It has sharp teeth.

4.

a. It has striped fur.

b. It has a hard shell.

Conexión con el hogar

QuerIdos familiares:

Estoy leyendo *Animal Moms and Dads* en la clase esta semana. Aprendí que todos los cuentos tienen una idea principal. La idea principal es sobre lo que trata el cuento. Los detalles me dan más información acerca de la idea principal. Este cuento narra cómo los animales mamás y papás cuidan a sus bebés. Las mamás les llevan comida a sus bebés. Los papás les quitan los bichos que tienen en la piel. ¡Los animales mamás y papás parecen cuidar de sus bebés como ustedes cuidan de mí!

Destrezas de la semana

Comprensión: idea principal y detalles

Fonética: palabras con el sonido de **o** como en *cot*

Ortografía: palabras con **o**

Nombre _____

(Fold here)

© Macmillan/McGraw-Hill

Ejercicio de palabras

PALABRAS DE VOCABULARIO

one   two   they   her   does

Recordar Piensa acerca del libro que estás leyendo esta semana. Usemos las palabras de arriba para hablar acerca de los padres de los animales y otros miembros de la familia.

PALABRAS DE ORTOGRAFÍA

hog   hot   log

top   hop   lot

Quitar letras Repite cada palabra que digo. Deletrea la palabra. Quita la primera letra de cada palabra y lee nuevamente en voz alta cada palabra. ¿Cómo suena la letra **o** en cada palabra? ¿Podemos encontrar otras palabras que tengan el mismo sonido?

Encuentra el animal

A continuación tenemos 5 detalles. Encierra en un círculo la ilustración que se corresponde con cada detalle. En la página siguiente, escribe las letras de la palabra que describe la ilustración. Lee hacia abajo la columna que está sombreada. Las letras formarán la idea principal.

1. It has whiskers.

2. You can see it in the zoo.

3. This is when it hunts.

4. These are very sharp.

5. It has black lines as part of its coat.

1. __ __ __ __ __ __

2. __ __ __ __ __ __

3. __ __ __ __ __ __

4. __ __ __ __ __ __

5. __ __ __ __ __ __

¡Escribe las letras y encuentra el animal! "All about a __ __ __ __ __ __ __" is the main idea.

Fox on a Rock

by Marsha Gilmore

illustrated by Aleksey Ivanov

Fox on a Rock

This page is intentionally blank.

Mom Fox is very sad.
Where is Bob Fox now?

2

© 2007 Macmillan/McGraw-Hill

This page is intentionally blank.

Fox on a Rock

Is Bob Fox in Frog's pond?
Bob is not in Frog's pond.

3

Ant can help Mom Fox.
Now Mom can see Bob Fox!

6

Is Bob Fox in Tom's box?
Bob is not in Tom's box.

4

Mom Fox is sad.
Mom sits on a rock.
Mom can use help.

5

Little Bears

by Melissa Rothman

Comprehension Check

Retell

Use a Main Idea Chart to help retell what you learned about bears.

Think and Compare

1. What can little bears do?
2. What can you do that little bears can do?
3. What can grownups do that children can not do?

16

Look at the big bear.
Look at her cubs.

2

They will be very big bears
one day, too.

15

The cubs will get big.

4

What can the two cubs do?
They can play.

The cubs can not.
Cubs are too little.

Little Bears

13

They can look
for food to eat.

Little Bears

A big bear can get a fish.

The cubs can rest.
They take a long nap.

9

11

The cubs can play
on the rocks.

Little Bears

Where are the
bears now?

What does this cub do?
This one rolls in the grass.

What does this cub do?
This one runs fast.

Dear Family Member:

I'm reading *Little Red Hen* in class this week. I learned that we can retell a story to make sure we understand it. *Little Red Hen* begins when Hen asks for help to plant some wheat. Dog, Pig, and Cat do not want to help, so Little Red Hen does it herself. The friends don't want to help water the wheat either. I wonder if they will help her do anything? I can retell the story by describing what happens in the order it happens.

This Week's Skills

Comprehension: retell

Phonics: the sound of e as in *ten*

Spelling: words with e

(fold here)

© Macmillan/McGraw-Hill

Word Workout

WORDS TO KNOW

who   some   of   no   eat

Story Time Use the words to tell me a story about how bread is made. Start with a seed and end with a loaf of bread in a store.

MY SPELLING WORDS

beg   get   hen   leg   let   men

Rhyme Time I'm going to ask you to spell each word. Which pairs of words rhyme? Can we think of other words that rhyme with *beg, get,* and *men?*

Name _____

Happy Dog

Let's talk about each picture. I'll help you read each one. When we are all done, you can retell our story.

My dog has

_____

First I have to

_____.

Then I have to

_____

I have to

_____.

Now we

_____.

96

Conexión con el hogar

Queridos familiares:

Estoy leyendo *Little Red Hen* en la clase esta semana. Aprendí que podemos verificar si entendimos un cuento cuando lo contamos de nuevo. El cuento *Little Red Hen* comienza cuando Hen pide ayuda para plantar trigo. Dog, Pig y Cat no quieren ayudar, entonces Little Red Hen lo hace sola. Los amigos tampoco quieren ayudar a regar el trigo. Me pregunto si la ayudarán a hacer algo. Puedo contar el cuento de nuevo al describir lo que pasa en el orden en que ocurren las cosas.

Destrezas de la semana

Comprensión: volver a contar

Fonética: el sonido de la e como en *ten*

Ortografía: palabras con e

Nombre _____

(fold here)

Ejercicio de palabras

PALABRAS DE VOCABULARIO

who   some   of   no   eat

Tiempo de cuentos Usa las palabras para contarme un cuento sobre cómo se hace el pan. Comienza con una semilla y termina con un pan en una panadería.

PALABRAS DE ORTOGRAFÍA

beg   get   hen   leg   let   men

Vamos a rimar Te pediré que deletrees cada palabra. ¿Cuáles son pares de palabras que riman? ¿Podemos pensar en otras palabras que riman con *beg, get* y *men*?

El perro feliz

Hablemos acerca de cada ilustración. Te ayudaré a leer cada una. Cuando terminemos, puedes contar de nuevo nuestro cuento.

My dog has

First I have to

Then I have to

I have to

Now we

Hen's Eggs

by Wiley Blevins
illustrated by Anthony Lewis

Hen's Eggs

This page is intentionally blank.

"Ben, can Mom fix eggs?"
"Yes, Meg. Get two eggs."

8

This page is intentionally blank.

Hen's Eggs

"We have one egg.
Get Hen's egg, Ben.
Get her egg."

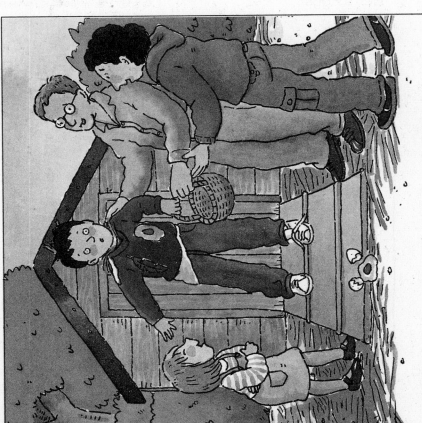

Mom will not fix eggs.
Mom will fix ham!

Does Hen have eggs?
Ben is in Hen's pen.
Hen is mad!

10

Hen's Eggs

Meg yells for Mom
and Dad.
They will help.

11

Food from the Farm

by Sara Tom

Comprehension Check

Retelling Chart

1	→	2
3	→	4
5	→	6

Retell

Use a Retelling Chart to retell this book.

Think and Compare

1. What things in this book do we get from the farm?

2. If you could visit a farm, what would you like to see?

3. Why are farms important for people?

16

Look at the farm.
What can you get
from a farm?

2

Food from the Farm

15

Food from the Farm

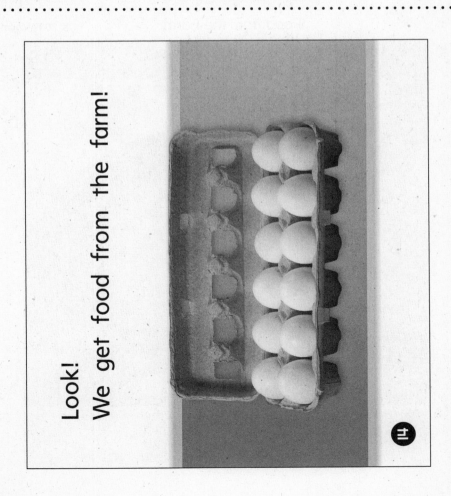

Look!
We get food from the farm!

Look at the cows.

4

13

We get milk from the cows.

5

Who will eat some of the corn?

12

Who will have some of
the milk?

Food from the Farm

Look! Now there is
no corn.

Food from the Farm

Look at the corn.

10

Look at the hen.
We get eggs from
the hen.

8

Who will eat some of
the eggs?

9

Dear Family Member:

I'm reading "A Prairie Dog Home" in class this week. I remember that every selection has a main idea. The main idea is what the selection is mostly about. Details tell more about the main idea. This selection tells how prairie dogs live. The author gives a lot of details about a prairie dog's home. Many prairie dogs live together in one home. In some ways, prairie dogs' homes are like our homes! They are different in r ways, too.

This Week's Skills

Comprehension: main and details

Phonics: the sound of **sh** and **th** as in *ship* ar *think*

Spelling: words with **s** and **th**

(fold here)

Name _____

Word Workout

WORDS TO KNOW

into   many   live   out

A Brand New Animal Let's make up a new animal that no one has ever seen before. We can compare it to a prairie dog. We'll use the words to describe the new animal.

MY SPELLING WORDS

fish   ship   shop

thank   thin   with

Two Equals One Sometimes two two letters stand for one sound. I'll give you a spelling word, and you can spell it. Then we can look for other words with the letters **sh** and **th**.

A Funny Farm

Let's help Mrs. Shin clean up her farm. Color the pictures of things that belong on the farm. Put an X on things that do not belong.

Now let's talk about the details that describe Mrs. Shin's farm.

Conexión con el hogar

Queridos familiares:

Estoy leyendo *A Prairie Dog Home* en la clase esta semana. Ya sé que cada selección tiene una idea principal. La idea principal es sobre lo que trata la selección. Los detalles ofrecen más información acerca de la idea principal. Esta selección habla sobre cómo viven los perros de las praderas. El autor da muchos detalles sobre el hogar de los perros de las praderas. Muchos de ellos viven juntos en un hogar. De alguna manera, ¡los hogares de los perros de las praderas son como nuestros hogares! Pero por otro lado, los hogares son diferentes también.

Destrezas de la semana

Comprensión: idea principal y detalles

Fonética: las sonidos sh y th como en *ship* y *think*

Ortografía: palabras con sh y th

Nombre _____

(fold here)

© Macmillan/McGraw-Hill

Ejercicio de palabras

PALABRAS DE VOCABULARIO

into   many   live   out

Un animal nuevo Inventemos un animal nuevo, uno que nunca nadie haya visto antes. Podemos compararlo con un perro de la pradera. Usaremos las palabras para describir al animal nuevo.

PALABRAS DE ORTOGRAFÍA

fish   ship   shop

thank   thin   with

Dos es igual a uno A veces dos letras juntas representan un sonido. Te voy a dar una palabra de ortografía y tú la deletreas. Luego, podemos buscar otras palabras con las letras **sh** y **th**.

Una granja divertida

Ayudemos a la señora Shin a limpiar su granja.
Colorea las cosas que sí pertenecen a la granja.
Coloca una X sobre las cosas que no
pertenecen a la granja.

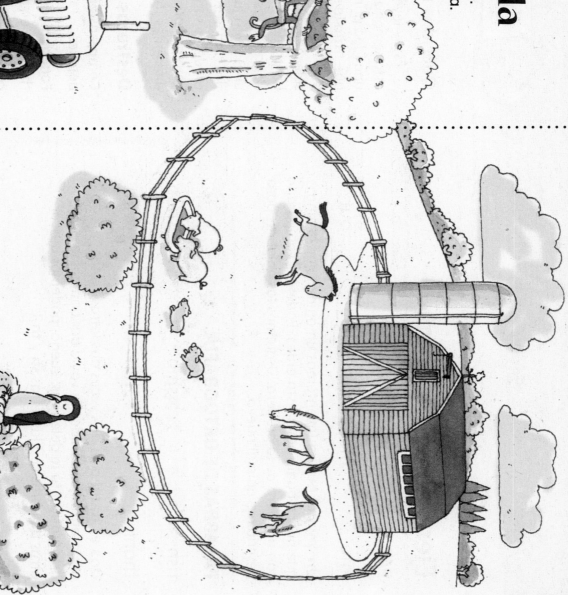

Hablemos sobre la granja de la
señora Shin.

This Fish, That Fish

by Maryann Dobeck

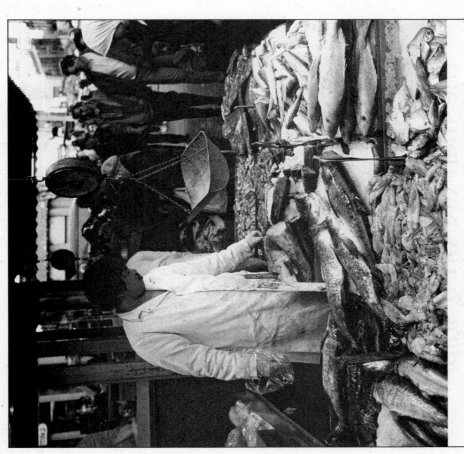

This shop sells fresh fish.
Get some fish to eat!

20

This is a fish tank.
It has lots of fish.
Can you see them?

14

This Fish, That Fish   © 2007 Macmillan/McGraw-Hill

The men are on a ship.
They fish with big nets.

19

Fish can eat a lot.
Who can help them?
This man gets food.

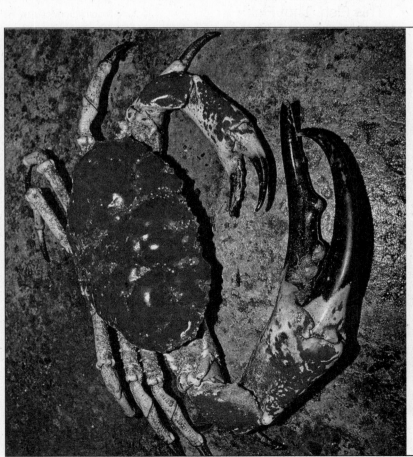

Is that a fish?
No, it is a crab.
It has a thin shell.

Some fish are thin.
This fish is fat!

This Fish, That Fish

This fish is fat, too.
This fish can puff up!

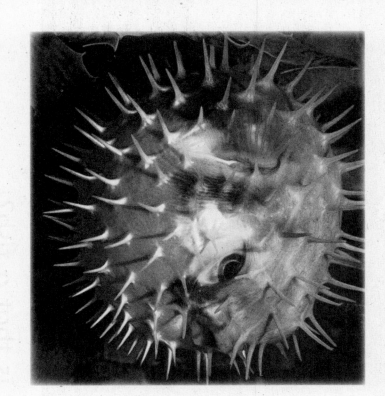

Birds

by Andrew Taylor

Comprehension Check

Retell

Look back at the pictures. Tell a partner what you learned about birds.

Think and Compare

1. What is the main idea of this book?
2. Where do you see birds?
3. Name 3 places where birds live.

16

Where do birds live?

2

Birds

Can you find birds
where you live?

15

Birds live in many places.

Birds

Birds live in many places.

4

This bird lives in a park.
It hops in the grass.

Birds

Other birds live
where it is cold.

13

The bird used twigs
to make a nest.
Look into the nest.
What do you see?

Birds

Some birds live
in the hot desert.

12

This bird lives
in the woods.
It will peck
a hole in
the tree.

6

The birds come back
to the land.
They make their nests
in the rocks.

11

Now the bird
has a nest
in the hole.

Birds

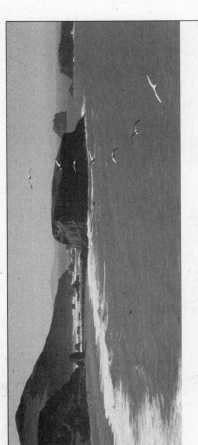

Some birds live
by the sea.
You can see them fly
out over the shore.
They fly out over the sea.

This bird lives
in a pond.

Its nest is in
the pond.
The nest is made
of wet grass.

Dear Family Member:

I'm reading *The Fun Kids' Band* in class this week. I can check if I understand a story by retelling it in my own words. In *The Fun Kids' Band*, a group of kids want to play in a band. They have to make their own instruments using old things they find in a box! I wonder what instruments they will play. When I know, I can retell the story by describing what happens in the order it happens.

This Week's Skills

Comprehension: retell

Phonics: the sound of u as in *sun*

Spelling: words with **u**

(fold here)

© Macmillan/McGraw-Hill

Name _____

Word Workout

WORDS TO KNOW

want	put	show
under	three	make

Double Up I'll give you two words. You can use both words in one sentence. I'll repeat words but in different pairs.

MY SPELLING WORDS

bug	cut	nut
rug	run	fun

u Can Do It I'll give you each word to spell. Then let's see what other three-letter words we can find with **u** in the middle.

Riddle Me This!

We're going to solve some riddles. I'll read the question, and we can try to answer it. The pictures will help. These riddles are tricky. We can turn the page upside down to check our answers.

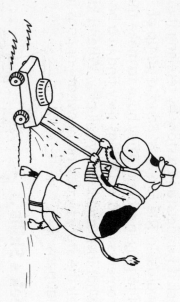

What do you call a cow that works in the yard?

A lawn moo-er!

Why do bees hum?

They don't know the words!

What happens to the duck who flies upside down?

He quacks up.

When is the best time to have lunch?

After breakfast.

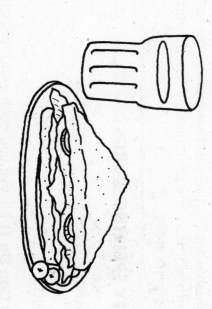

Queridos familiares:

Estoy leyendo *The Fun Kids' Band* en la clase esta semana. Puedo verificar si entiendo el cuento cuando lo cuento de nuevo con mis propias palabras. En el cuento *The Fun Kids' Band*, un grupo de niños quiere tocar en una banda. ¡Ellos tienen que fabricar sus propios instrumentos usando cosas viejas que encuentran en una caja! Me pregunto qué instrumentos van a tocar. Cuando lo sepa, puedo contar el cuento de nuevo y describir lo que pasa en el orden que ocurren las cosas.

Destrezas de la semana

Comprensión: volver a contar

Fonética: el sonido de la u como en *sun*

Ortografía: palabras con u

Nombre _____

(Fold here)

Ejercicio de palabras

PALABRAS DE VOCABULARIO

want	put	show
under	three	make

En pares Te voy a dar dos palabras. Puedes usar ambas palabras en una misma oración. Luego, repetiré palabras pero en pares diferentes.

PALABRAS DE ORTOGRAFÍA

bug	cut	nut
rug	run	fun

Tú puedes hacerlo Te voy a dar cada palabra para deletrear. Luego, veamos qué otras palabras de tres letras podemos encontrar con la letra u en el medio.

¡Adivina esto!

Vamos a resolver algunas adivinanzas. Voy a leer una pregunta y vamos a intentar responderla. Los dibujos nos ayudarán. Estas adivinanzas son difíciles. Podemos rotar la página para verificar nuestras respuestas.

What do you call a cow that works in the yard?

A lawn moo-er!

Why do bees hum?

They don't know the words!

What happens to the duck who flies upside down?

He quacks up.

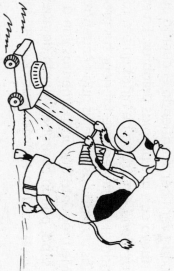

When is the best time to have lunch?

After breakfast.

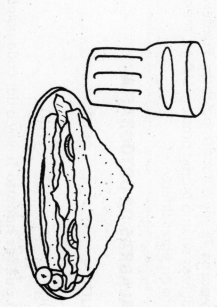

Just for Fun!

by Anna Keyes

This page is intentionally blank.

Where do Ed and Liz live?
They run and play here.
This band is a lot of fun!

22

This page is intentionally blank.

It is hot in the sun.
Kids jump in and
get wet.

Just for Fun!

Kris sees many ducks.
He drops bits of crust.
It is just for fun!

Kids can hit and run.
Gus hit it up, up, up.
It went into a mitt.

Just for Fun!

Kids jump up and
jump out.
It is fun, fun, fun!

Let's Put on a Show

by Ellen Catala
illustrated by Nancy Davis

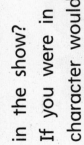

Comprehension Check

Retell the Story

Use a Retelling Chart to help you retell the story.

Retelling Chart		
1 →	2	
3 →	4	
5 →	6	

Think and Compare

1. What animal was Dan in the show?

2. If you were in this show, what character would you like to be?

3. Why do people go to see shows?

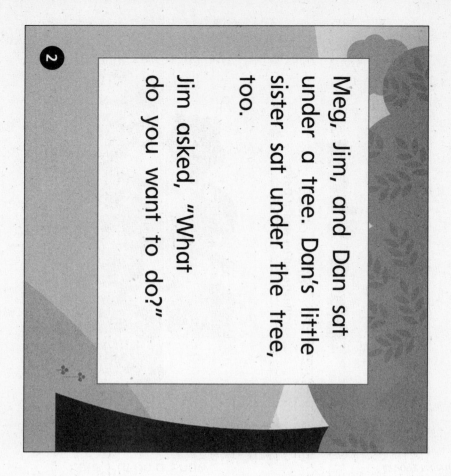

2

Meg, Jim, and Dan sat under a tree. Dan's little sister sat under the tree, too.

Jim asked, "What do you want to do?"

15

Dan's little sister said, "I am a lion. I can eat you."

The wolf ran and ran!

Everyone clapped.

3

Then Dan ran to
the brick house.

"Little Pig, let me in,"
he said.

14

Meg said, "I want to put on a show."

4

Jim said, "I am not a pig. I am a crocodile. I can eat you."

13

Let's Put on a Show

5

Dan ran to the stick house.

"Little Pig, let me in," he said.

12

Jim and Dan said,
"Yes! What show should
we put on?"

6

Meg said, "I am not a pig.
I am a bear. I can eat you."

11

Then Dan's little sister said, "I want the Three Little Pigs!"

7

Then they put on a show. Dan was the wolf. He went to the straw house.

"Little Pig, let me in," he said.

10

8

Meg, Dan, and Jim had to make up lines. They had to make noses. They had to make three houses.

9

Dear Family Member:

I'm reading On My Way to School in class this week. I learned that things in a story happen in order, or sequence. A little boy is trying to get to school, but all sorts of animals make him late. First, there is a pig, and then there is a duck. I don't know what will happen next. Does the little boy get to school on time?

This Week's Skills

Comprehension: sequence

Phonics: the sounds of **bl, cl,** and **fl**

Spelling: words with **bl, cl,** and **fl**

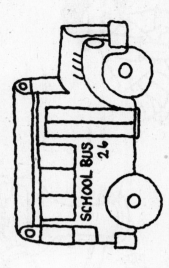

SCHOOL BUS 26

Name _____

(fold here)

Word Workout

WORDS TO KNOW

today	way	school
late	away	why

Story Time Let's create a story about a child who was *late* for *school*. We can talk about what happened on the way to school. You can write down the sentences using the words.

MY SPELLING WORDS

black	block	clock	flag
clip	flip		

Sort the Words Let's fold a piece of lined paper into three columns. Write **bl, cl,** and **fl** at the top of the columns. Write your new spelling words in the correct list. Then let's add other words that begin with the same letters.

Minna's Morning

It's time to get up, Minna! Look at the picture with a star above it. What is happening? Put the number 1 in the picture. Let's talk about the other pictures. What do you think Minna does right after she gets up? We can put the number 2 in that picture. Let's number all the pictures to show how Minna gets ready for school.

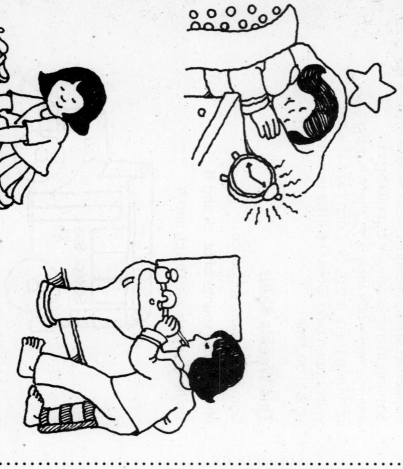

Tell about Minna's morning.
Tell the steps in order.

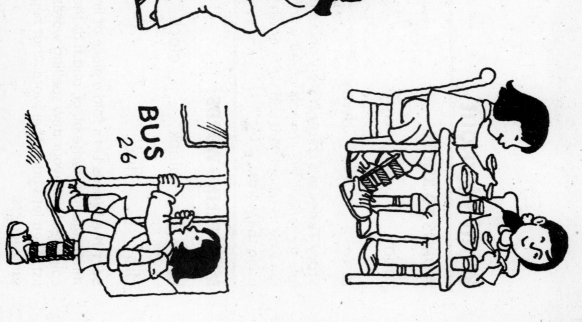

Conexión con el hogar

Queridos familiares:

Estoy leyendo *On My Way to School* en la clase esta semana. Aprendí que las cosas en un cuento ocurren en orden, o en secuencia. Este cuento está escrito en rima. Un niño pequeño trata de llegar a la escuela pero todo tipo de animales lo atrasan. Primero aparece un puerco y luego aparece un pato. No sé lo que pasará después. ¿Llegará a tiempo el niño a la escuela?

Destrezas de la semana

Comprensión: orden de los sucesos

Fonética: los sonidos de bl, cl y fl

Ortografía: palabras con bl, cl y fl

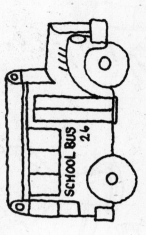

© Macmillan/McGraw-Hill

(fold here)

Nombre _____

Ejercicio de palabras

PALABRAS DE VOCABULARIO

today   way   school

late   away   why

Tiempo de cuentos Vamos a hacer un cuento sobre un niño quien estuvo *late* para *school*. Podemos hablar sobre qué ocurrió en la manera a escuela. Puedes escribir las oraciones con las palabras que usamos.

PALABRAS DE ORTOGRAFÍA

black   block   clock   flag

clip   flip

Clasificar las palabras Doblemos una hoja de papel con renglones en tres partes para formar tres columnas. Escribe **bl, cl** y **fl** en la parte superior de las columnas. Escribe tus palabras nuevas de ortografía en la columna correcta. Luego, agreguemos otras palabras que comienzan con las mismas letras.

145

La mañana de Minna

Mira la ilustración que tiene una estrella arriba. ¿Qué está pasando? Pon el número 1 en la ilustración. Hablemos de las otras ilustraciones. ¿Qué hace Minna justo después de levantarse? Coloquemos el número 2 en esa ilustración. Coloquemos números sobre cada ilustración para mostrar cómo Minna se prepara para ir a la escuela.

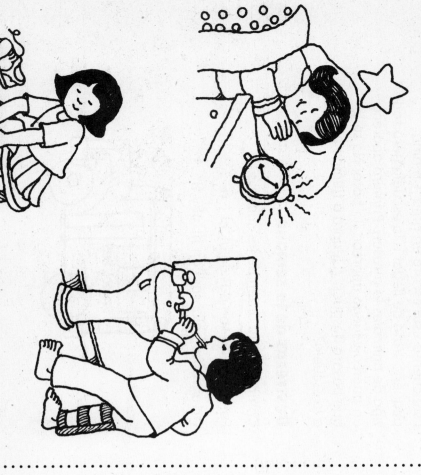

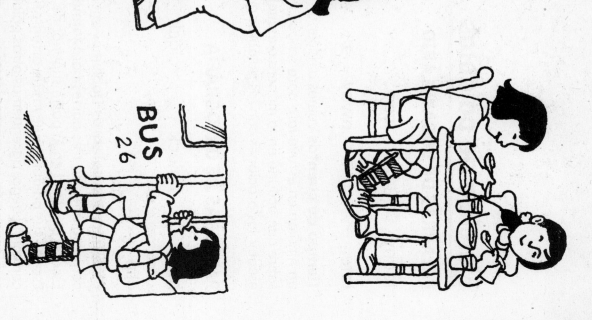

Tell about Minna's morning.
Tell the steps in order.

Come On, Clem!

by Lucy Floyd

illustrated by Mick Reid

Come On, Clem!

This page is intentionally blank.

"Let's plan a show!"
yells the Math Club.
"Come on, Clem!"

This page is intentionally blank.

Clem tells them NO.
Ann tells Clem,
"You can dress up!"

Clem is under it!
"It's a bug," he yells.
"It has six legs!"

2+2=4
4+4=8
6+6=12

"OK, then," Clem nods.
"I want three desks."

© 2007 Macmillan/McGraw-Hill

Clem cuts a flat blob.
Did Clem make a sled?
Can Clem put it on?

Late for School

by David Michaels

illustrated by Erika LeBarre

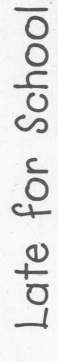

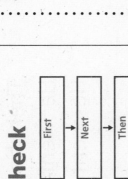

Comprehension Check

Retell the Story

Use a Sequence Chart to help you retell the story.

First
↓
Next
↓
Then
↓
Last

Think and Compare

1. What did Elephant do to get ready for school?

2. What do you do after school?

3. Which days are school days?

16

2

Then he went to find Bear.
He went to find Lion.
He went to find Mouse too.

"Let's play!" he said.

15

Elephant sat up. He looked at the clock.

"Oh, no! I will be late for school!"

Elephant went home.
He put his books away.
He put his lunch away.

Elephant got dressed.
He got his books.
He got his lunch.
He put them
in his blue backpack.

4

13

Late for School

5

Mouse laughed and laughed.

He said, "We can not go to school today. It is not a school day."

12

Elephant ran down the street.
On the way, he saw Bear.

"Why are you playing?"
asked Elephant. "We are late
for school today!"

9

Elephant asked, "Why are you
playing? We are late for
school today."

11

Bear said, "Go away!"

Late for School

7

Then Elephant ran by the playground. On his way, he saw Mouse.

10

Elephant ran by the firehouse.
On the way, he saw Lion.

"Why are you playing?"
asked Elephant. "We are late
for school today."

8

Lion said, "Go away!"

9

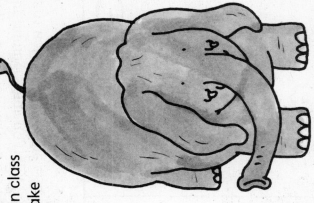

Dear Family Member:

I'm reading *Kate's Game* in class this week. I'm learning to make predictions while reading. A prediction is a good guess about what will happen next in a story. In this story, Kate makes up the best games. Some friends have come to play, but they get stuck in the mud. What will happen next?

This Week's Skills

Comprehension: make predictions

Phonics: the sound of a as in *bake* and *date*

Spelling: words with a-e

·········· (Fold here) ··········

Word Workout

WORDS TO KNOW

hello   could   walk   pull   all   oh

What's Missing? Let's talk about the words above and what they mean. Then I'll say a sentence with a missing word. You can say the sentence putting in the missing word.

SPELLING WORDS

take   make   late   came   game   gate

Write It Right Look at the vowels in the words. How are all the words alike? Write each word in the air with your arm as you spell it. Then write it on a piece of paper.

Name _____

What Will Happen Next?

Let's play a game. We'll start at the box that says GO, where the girl is planting seeds. Write the number two on the picture that shows what you think will happen next. As we play, we do not have to include all the pictures in our story. Our numbers may go right, left, or up and down. We'll take turns until we reach the end of the story.

Queridos familiares:

Estoy leyendo *Kate's Game* en la clase esta semana. Aprendo a hacer predicciones mientras leo. Una predicción es hacer una buena suposición acerca de lo que va a pasar en el cuento. En este cuento, Kate inventa los mejores juegos. Un grupo de amigos vienen a jugar, pero se quedan atascados en el lodo. ¿Que pasará despues?

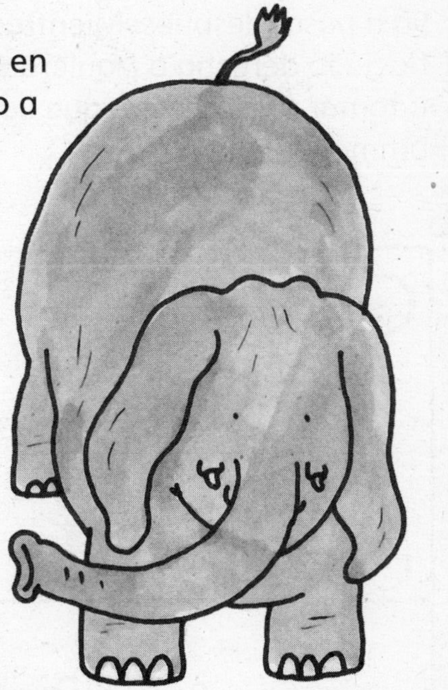

Destrezas de la semana

Comprensión: hacer predicciones

Fonética: el sonido de a como en *bake*

Ortografía: palabras con a-e

(fold here)

© Macmillan/McGraw-Hill

Ejercicio de palabras

PALABRAS DE VOCABULARIO

hello   could   walk   pull   all   oh

¿Qué falta? Hablemos de las palabras de arriba y de lo que significan. Luego, voy a decir una oración con una palabra que falta. Puedes decir la oración agregando la palabra que falta.

PALABRAS DE ORTOGRAFÍA

take   make   late   came   game   gate

Escribe la palabra correctamente Observa las vocales en las palabras. ¿En qué se parecen todas las palabras? Escribe cada palabra en el aire con tu mano mientras la deletreas. Luego, escríbela en una hoja de papel.

Nombre

¿Qué va a pasar después?

Vamos a jugar un juego. Vamos a comenzar en la casilla que dice **GO**, donde la niña está plantando semillas. Dibuja una flecha hacia la casilla que muestre lo que tú crees que va a pasar después. Mientras jugamos, las flechas pueden ir hacia la derecha o izquierda, o hacia arriba o abajo. Vamos a tomar turnos hasta que lleguemos al final del cuento en la última hilera.

Jane and Wade

by Maryann Dobeck

illustrated by Hector Borlasca

Jane and Wade

This page is intentionally blank.

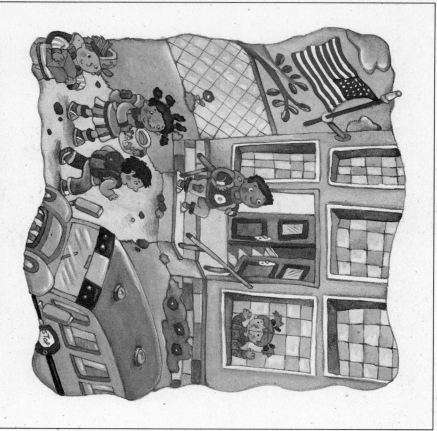

Today is a big pet show.
It is at the Tate School.
It's in Miss Hale's class.

2

Jane and Wade

This page is intentionally blank.

Jane and Wade

Gale came with pet fish.

Shane came with his dog.

Dave came with a snake!

3

Jane's frog got away!

Where did Wade end up?

He jumped in the fish tank.

What a way to have fun!

6

Jane came with a frog.
"His name is Wade,"
said Jane.
"Wade is the best pet."

4

"Why?" Gale asked.
Just then Wade jumped up.
Jane yelled, "Get Wade!"
But Jane was too late.

5

Friends Can Help

by Su-Mi Park

Comprehension Check

Retell

Use a Predictions Chart to check your predictions about the book.

What I Predict	What Happens

Think and Compare

1. Look back at page 13. What will the person say who gets the card?

2. Have you ever helped a friend? What did you do? Has a friend ever helped you? What did the friend do?

3. Who else besides friends helps people in your town? How do they help?

16

How could you help a friend? You could help a friend do many things.

Friends Can Help

Look at all the ways to be a good friend!

You could help one friend.
You could help many friends.
You could do many things
to help.

Friends Can Help

Could you be a friend?
Oh, yes! Oh, yes!

You could help to plant a garden. You could put in all kinds of plants.

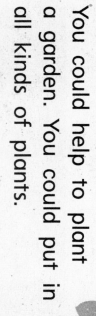

The boy makes a hole for a little plant.

4

You could make a card for a friend and write "Hello."

A card can tell someone you care.

13

You could wave
"Hello" to a friend.

Friends Can Help

© 2007 Macmillan/McGraw-Hill

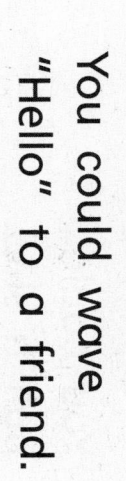

You could help a friend
pick a pumpkin.

Did you ever pick up a
pumpkin this big?

You could help a friend read a book. You could help a friend read all the words.

⊙ Did you ever help a friend read?

You could pull a sled.

11

This boy shows his friends what to do.

You could help a friend
play a game on
the computer.

You could help a friend
pull a wagon.

You could be a friend to pets.
You could walk a dog.

This girl takes her dog for a walk.

Friends Can Help

You could feed a fish.

Fish need little bits of food.

Dear Family Member:

I'm reading *Kids Can Help* in class this week. I learned that I should think about how things are alike and different. In *Kids Can Help*, one boy helps his dad cook. A girl helps her mom make bread. The boy and the girl are alike. They are also different.

This Week's Skills

Comprehension: compare and contrast

Phonics: the sounds of **sn** and **sl**

Spelling: words with **sn** and **sp**

.... (fold here) ....

© Macmillan/McGraw-Hill

Name _____

Word Workout

WORDS TO KNOW

girl   boy   together   when

people   care   water

Tell Me Let's say the words together aloud. Then you can tell me a story about a little girl and boy who like to help. See how many of the words you can use in your story.

SPELLING WORDS

snake   spill   sled   snap   slip   spin

Listening Time Listen to each word I say. Then say the sounds you hear at the beginning of each word. Finally, spell the word as you write it.

Same or Different Concentration

We're going to compare and contrast by playing "Concentration." Here's how:

We'll make circles to cover each box.

You can take two circles off the board.

If your pictures match, take the circles off the board and put an **X** on a piece of paper.

If your pictures do not match, try to remember which picture is in which square.

Then put the circles back on the board.

Then I'll go and do the same thing.

We'll take turns. When there are no more matches, the game is over. Who has the most matches?

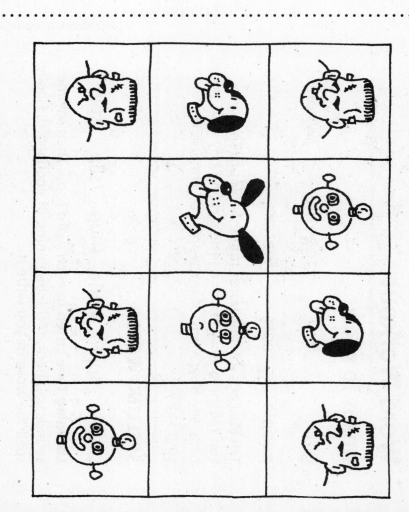

Queridos familiares:

Estoy leyendo *Kids Can Help* en la clase esta semana. Aprendí que debo pensar acerca de cómo las cosas son parecidas o diferentes. En el cuento *Kids Can Help*, un niño ayuda a su padre a cocinar y una niña ayuda a su madre a hacer pan. El niño y la niña se parecen. También se diferencian.

Destrezas de la semana

Comprensión: comparar y contrastar

Fonética: los sonidos sn y sl

Ortografía: palabras con sn y sp

Nombre _____

Ejercicio de palabras

PALABRAS DE VOCABULARIO

girl   boy   together   when

people   care   water

Dime Decimos las palabras en voz alta. Luego dime un cuento sobre un niño y una niña que le gusta ayudar. Veamos cuantas palabras puedes usar en su cuento.

PALABRAS DE ORTOGRAFÍA

snake   spill   sled   snap   slip   spin

Vamos a escuchar Escucha cada palabra que digo. Luego, di los sonidos que escuchas al principio de cada palabra. Por último, deletrea la palabra mientras la escribes.

Concentración: igual o diferente

Vamos a comparar y contrastar jugando a un juego de concentración. Lee a continuación cómo jugar:

- Vamos a hacer círculos para cubrir cada casilla.

- Puedes quitar dos círculos del tablero.

- Si tus dibujos son iguales, escribe una x en una hoja de papel.

- Si tus dibujos son diferentes, trata de recordar qué dibujo está en esa casilla. Luego, coloca los círculos de nuevo en el tablero.

- Vamos a tomar turnos. El juego termina cuando no queden más dibujos iguales. Gana quien tenga la mayor cantidad de x.

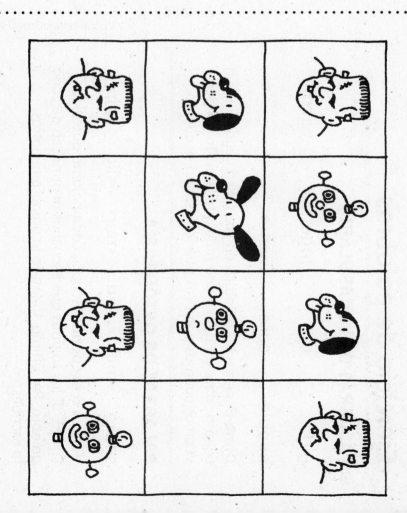

Slap Hello!

by Ana Ruiz

Jane and Wade

This page is intentionally blank.

What ways can we tell hello?
Let's all stand and wave.
Let's pull off hats.
Let's snap and clap hands.

8

This page is intentionally blank.

Tim can walk up to Gramps.
Gramps has a big grin.
Gramps could wave a hand.
But Gramps pats and hugs.

Jane and Wade

Kiss, kiss, kiss!
Step up and get a quick hug.
Oh, Mom has a big, big grin!

Will the men slap backs?
No, the men will just grin
and clasp hands.
Then they will chat.

10

"Stop and spend a little
time with me!"
The pals will not hug and kiss.
But they will shake hands.

11

Holiday Fun

by Max Aron

Comprehension Check

Retell

Use an Alike and Different Chart to tell how holidays are alike and different.

Different   Alike   Different

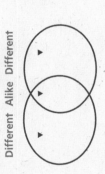

Think and Compare

1. Which holidays have parades?

2. Which holiday in the book did you like best?

3. Do you think it is important to celebrate holidays? Why or why not?

16

People all over like holidays.
People come together
to do things on holidays.

2

They wave flags that
are red, white, and blue.
Holidays are fun!

15

It is Thanksgiving Day in the United States.

People have holiday fun!

3

It is the Fourth of July in the United States.

This country is having a birthday, too. Boys and girls are in a parade.

14

4

Today people give thanks
for the things they have.

The flag is red, white,
and green.

13

It is Thanksgiving Day in Korea.

They have lots of good things to eat.

5

It is Independence Day in Mexico.

Today this country is having a birthday. This boy stops to wave his flag.

12

6

Today boys and girls are together at a parade.

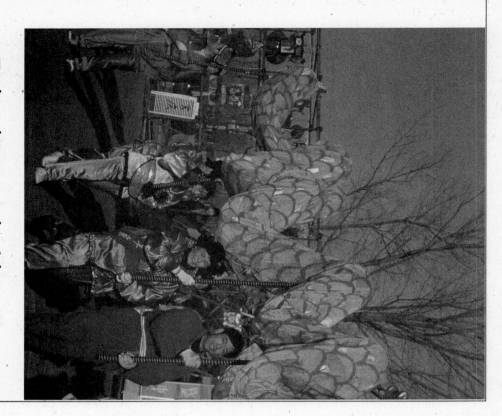

The kites are shaped like fish. But the kites will not go in the water. They swim in the sky.

11

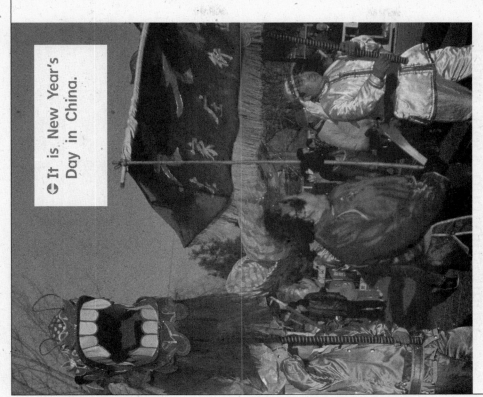

It is New Year's Day in China.

It is fun when the big dragon comes along.

Holiday Fun

It is Children's Day in Japan.

Today people fly kites.
They take care of the kites.

Today boys and girls dance
and spin. They have ribbons
when they dance.

© 2007 Macmillan/McGraw-Hill

They take good care of
the ribbons.

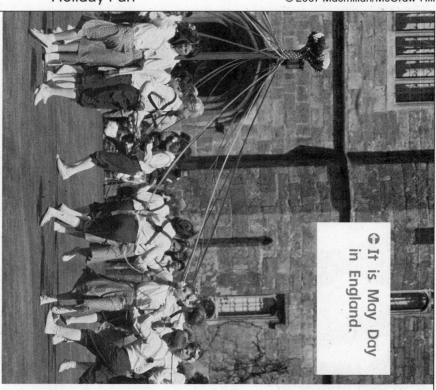

It is May Day
in England.

Dear Family Member:

I'm reading "Short Shadows, Long Shadows" in class this week. It's about what makes a shadow long or short. That's the main idea. The ways that light change the shape of shadows are the details. Can we go look for our shadows?

This Week's Skills

Comprehension: main idea and details

Phonics: the sound of ch and wh

Spelling: words with ch and wh

·············(fold here)·············

© Macmillan/McGraw-Hill

Name _____

Word Workout

WORDS TO KNOW

light   our   would   your   again

Two in One! Make up a sentence for each word. Maybe you can use two of the words in one sentence!

SPELLING WORDS

whale   catch   match   chin   chop   whip

Sort the Words Let's fold a piece of lined paper in half. Write ch and wh at the top of each half. Then write your spelling words under the correct letters. Add a word that begins or ends with the same letters to the two lists.

Whitney's Favorite Animal

Whitney went to the zoo with her dad. Which animal did Whitney like best? We can find out by coloring the puzzle. Let's use orange for the spaces showing what lives at a zoo. Let's use brown for the other spaces.

In the space below, draw something else Whitney may have seen at the zoo.

Conexión con el hogar

Queridos familiares:

Estoy leyendo *Short Shadows, Long Shadows* en la clase esta semana. El cuento habla acerca de lo que hace que una sombra sea larga o corta. Ésa es la idea principal. El cuento nos cuenta las maneras en que la luz hace que cambie la forma de las sombras. Esos son los detalles. ¿Podemos ir a ver nuestras sombras?

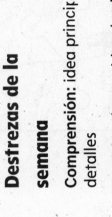

Destrezas de la semana

Comprensión: idea principal detalles

Fonética: los sonidos de ch y wh

Ortografía: palabras con ch y wh

(fold here)

© Macmillan/McGraw-Hill

Ejercicio de palabras

PALABRAS DE VOCABULARIO

light   our   would   your   again

¡Dos en una! Haz una oración para cada palabra. ¡Quizás puedas usar dos de las palabras en una oración!

PALABRAS DE ORTOGRAFÍA

whale   catch   match   chin   chop   whip

Clasifica las palabras Doblemos una hoja de papel con renglones a la mitad. Escribe **ch** y **wh** en la parte superior de cada mitad. Luego, escribe tus palabras de ortografía en la lista correcta. Agrega una palabra que comience o termine con las mismas letras.

Nombre _____

El animal favorito de Whitney

Whitney fue al zoológico con su padre. ¿Qué animal le gustó más a Whitney? Podemos averiguarlo si coloreamos el rompecabezas. Usemos el color anaranjado para los espacios que representan a los animales que viven en el zoológico. Usemos el color marrón para los otros espacios.

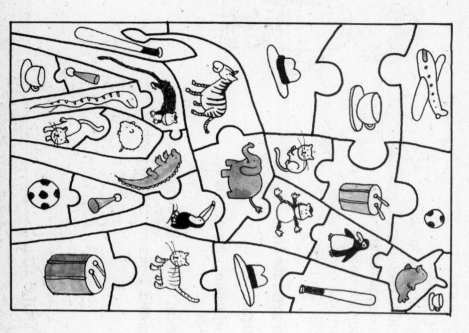

En el espacio de abajo, dibuja alguna otra cosa que Whitney pudo haber visto en el zoológico.

Such a Grand Day!

by Anna Keyes

The sun sets in the west.
I can see pink and red.
I had such fun today!

20

The big sun is up at six.
People stretch in bed and
then get up.
Let's check in with them.

14

Get together and grin.
Play a game of chess.
Pitch and catch with
a pal.

19

Whip up a batch of buns.
I wish I had a hot
baked bun. Yum!
Which one can I pick?

Such a Grand Day!

Kids check the lunch case.
Munch on fish and chips!
Grab a sandwich!

Kids can take care of a pet.
Dogs and cats get some
fresh water.
When will the pets get fed?

16

Kids chat in a bunch.
One boy and girl just
came on the bus.
Don't be late for class!

17

The Groundhog's Shadow

by Ben Wilson

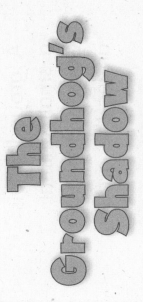

Comprehension Check

Retell

Look back at the pictures in this book. Tell a partner what you learned about groundhogs.

Think and Compare

1. What happens if the sun is out? What happens if it is not out?

2. Why would you be happy to know that spring is here?

3. Groundhog Day is a tradition. It comes every year. People do the same thing on that day each year. Why do you think people have traditions?

16

A groundhog is a small animal. Groundhogs dig dens under the ground.

A groundhog uses its claws to dig.

The Groundhog's Shadow

There are fireworks to celebrate Groundhog Day.

Groundhogs nap in dens much of the winter.

A groundhog has a warm coat of fur.

Will winter last six more weeks?

The groundhog did not see its shadow.
The people are glad.
Spring is here at last!

Now this groundhog
is getting up from
a long winter's nap.
Sometimes a groundhog
sees its shadow
when it comes out.

When do you see
your shadow?

Groundhog Day has been celebrated
for over one hundred years.

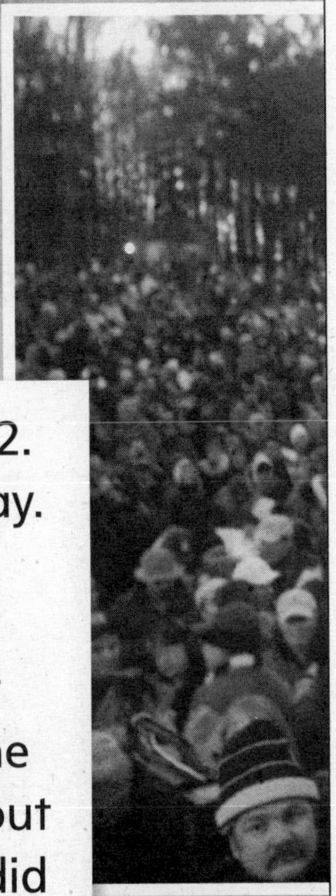

The Groundhog's Shadow

6 There is still snow on the ground.

Today is February 2.
It is Groundhog Day.

People have come
to catch a look at
this groundhog. The
groundhog came out
of its den. What did
the groundhog see?

What makes a shadow?

Sun makes light and light makes a shadow.

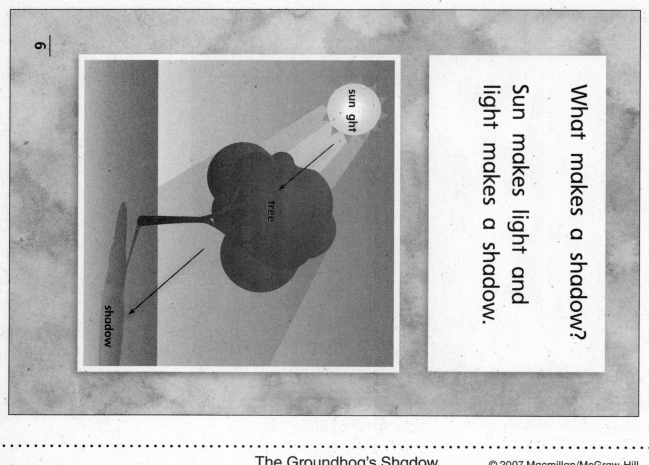

sun ght

tree

shadow

The groundhog will not go back into its den. Some people think this means that spring is here again.

When spring comes, flowers start to bloom.

11

When the sun is out, we can see our shadows. We would not see our shadows if the sun was not out.

↻ These boys are looking at their shadows.

7

↻ This groundhog does not see a shadow.

If the sun is not out, the groundhog will not see its shadow.

10

This groundhog is coming out of its den. The groundhog will see its shadow if the sun is out.

⊙ This groundhog has a shadow.

Then the groundhog will go back into its den again. Some people think that means there will be six more weeks of winter.

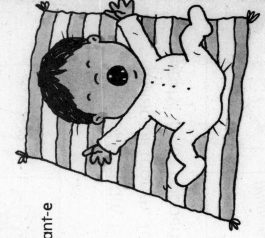

Dear Family Member:

I'm reading a play called *Smile, Mike!* in class this week. I know that when something happens in a story, I wonder what will happen next. In *Smile, Mike!* Mike keeps crying. Juan brings him a toy, but Mike cries. Then Ana sings, but Mike cries. I predict that Baby Mike will cry when the next person tries to make him smile.

This Week's Skills

Comprehension: make predictions

Phonics: i as in *kite* and *line*

Spelling: words with i-consonant-e

© Macmillan/McGraw-Hill

·······(fold here)·······

Name _____

Word Workout

WORDS TO KNOW

how	there
more	funny	so	call

Story Time I'm going to ask you what each word means. Then we can take turns using one of the words in a sentence. We'll listen to each other carefully to build a story with the sentences.

SPELLING WORDS

bike   hide   like   mine   ride   spike

Crossword Time Write one spelling word. Then cross it with another spelling word using the letter **i**. We can make other pairs with **i** to keep on playing.

Example:

	d	
s	i	d	e
	m	
	e	

What Happens Next?

Let's read each scene below and predict what will happen next. Then you can color the picture that matches our prediction.

1. Chris is learning how to rollerskate. He forgets to wear his knee pads. What happens next?

2. Monica's birthday is in April, and it has been raining all month. Tomorrow is her birthday party. What happens next?

3. The baby gets upset when he's hungry. This morning Mom is taking longer to prepare his bottle. What happens next?

4. Jasmine loves animals. The teacher asks her where she would like to go for a field trip. What happens next?

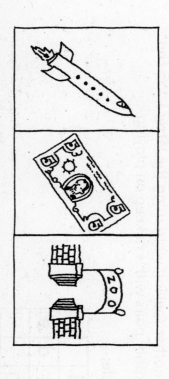

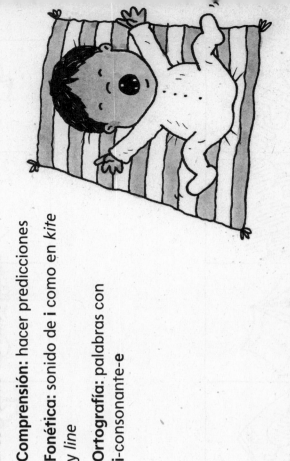

Conexión con el hogar

Queridos familiares:

Estoy leyendo una obra de teatro que se llama *Smile, Mike!* en la clase esta semana. Sé que cuando algo ocurre en un relato, me pregunto qué va a pasar después. En *Smile, Mike!*, Mike llora y llora. Juan le lleva un juguete, pero Mike llora. Luego Ana canta, pero Baby Mike llora. Predigo que Mike va a llorar cuando la próxima persona trate de hacerlo reír.

Destrezas de la semana

Comprensión: hacer predicciones

Fonética: sonido de i como en *kite* y *line*

Ortografía: palabras con i-consonante-e

(fold here)

© Macmillan/McGraw-Hill

Ejercicio de palabras

PALABRAS DE VOCABULARIO

how	there	so
more	funny	call

Tiempo de cuentos Voy a preguntarte lo que significa cada palabra. Luego, turnémonos para usar una palabra en una oración. Armemos juntos un relato con las oraciones.

PALABRAS DE ORTOGRAFÍA

bike	hide	like	mine	ride	spike

Tiempo de crucigramas Escribe una palabra de ortografía con letras grandes. Luego, crúzala con otra palabra de ortografía usando en común la letra i. Agreguemos otras palabras con i para seguir jugando.

Ejemplo:

d		
s	i	d	e
	m		
	e		

Nombre _____

Carrera de predicciones

¡Juguemos una carrera! Coloca una moneda de cinco centavos en la casilla que dice GO. Tira la moneda. Si sale "heads" puedes mover dos espacios. Si sale "tails" puedes mover un espacio. Observa el dibujo en la casilla en donde cayó tu moneda. Piensa acerca del dibujo en la casilla en donde cayó tu moneda. Luego, me tocará a mí y tiraré una moneda de cinco centavos. Podemos tomar turnos. Gana el primero que llega a la casilla que dice FINISH.

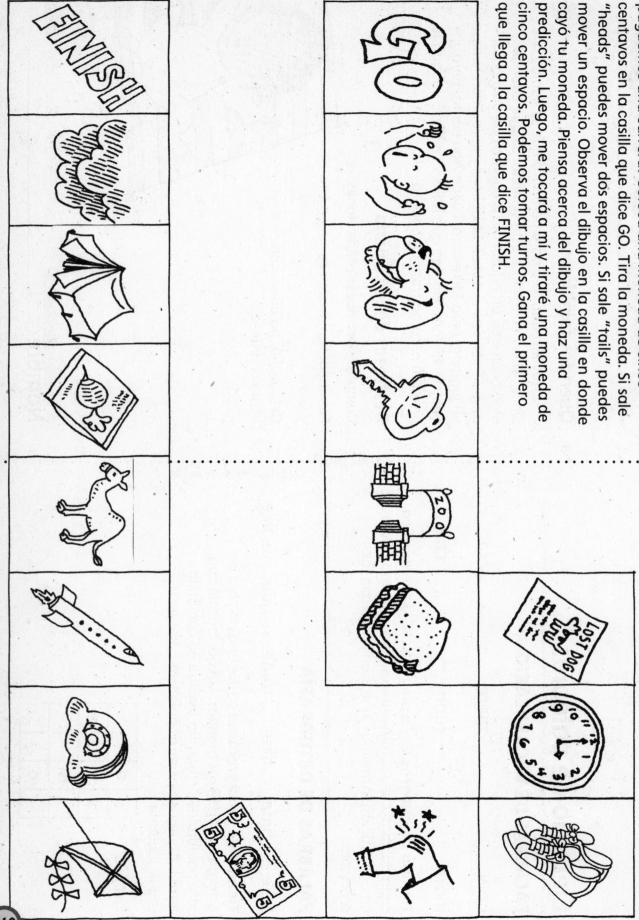

Job Time for the Pines

by Liz Ray

illustrated by R. W. Alley

Job Time for the Pines

This page is intentionally blank.

Mom and Dad must rest.

"Let's switch our jobs,"
Mike and Kim tell them.

"Fine," nod Mom and Dad.

22

This page is intentionally blank.

"Would you like a snack?"
Mike asks Dad.

Dad takes a bite.
"This is not ripe!"

Job Time for the Pines

Kim wipes up the suds.
"I must rest," she whines.

"It's time to switch back
again," smiles Mom.

Mom rides Kim's bike.
"Your bike isn't my size,"
Mom tells Kim.
Kim smiles at Mom.

24

Dad must make Mike's bed.
"Let's make it line up,"
Dad tells Mike.
But Dad bumps the light.

25

My Little Brother

by Emily Banks

Illustrated by Diane Paterson

Comprehension Check

Retell the Story

Use a Predictions Chart to check your predictions about the story.

What I Predict	What Happens

Think and Compare

1. What will Beth probably do the next time Sam wants to play with her? Why?

2. Who do you like to play with in your family? What do you like to play?

3. What games are fun for families to play together?

16

My name is Beth.
I am six.

2

And I like to do
what Sam likes to do.

15

This is my little brother.
I call him Sam.

3

There was Sam
playing on the rug.
I sat down there
and played with
his toys, too.
Sam likes to do
what I like to do.

4

Sam likes to do
what I like to do.
I like to paint
funny dinosaurs.
Sam likes to paint, too.

4

My Little Brother

Then I went to see.

13

I like to make things
with blocks.
He likes blocks, too.

5

I played dress up.

"How is Sam doing?"
I said.

12

I like to play dress up.
Sam likes to play dress up, too.

6

I made more nice things with blocks.

"What could Sam be doing?" I wondered.

11

I went back and painted
more funny dinosaurs.

"What is Sam doing?"
I wondered.

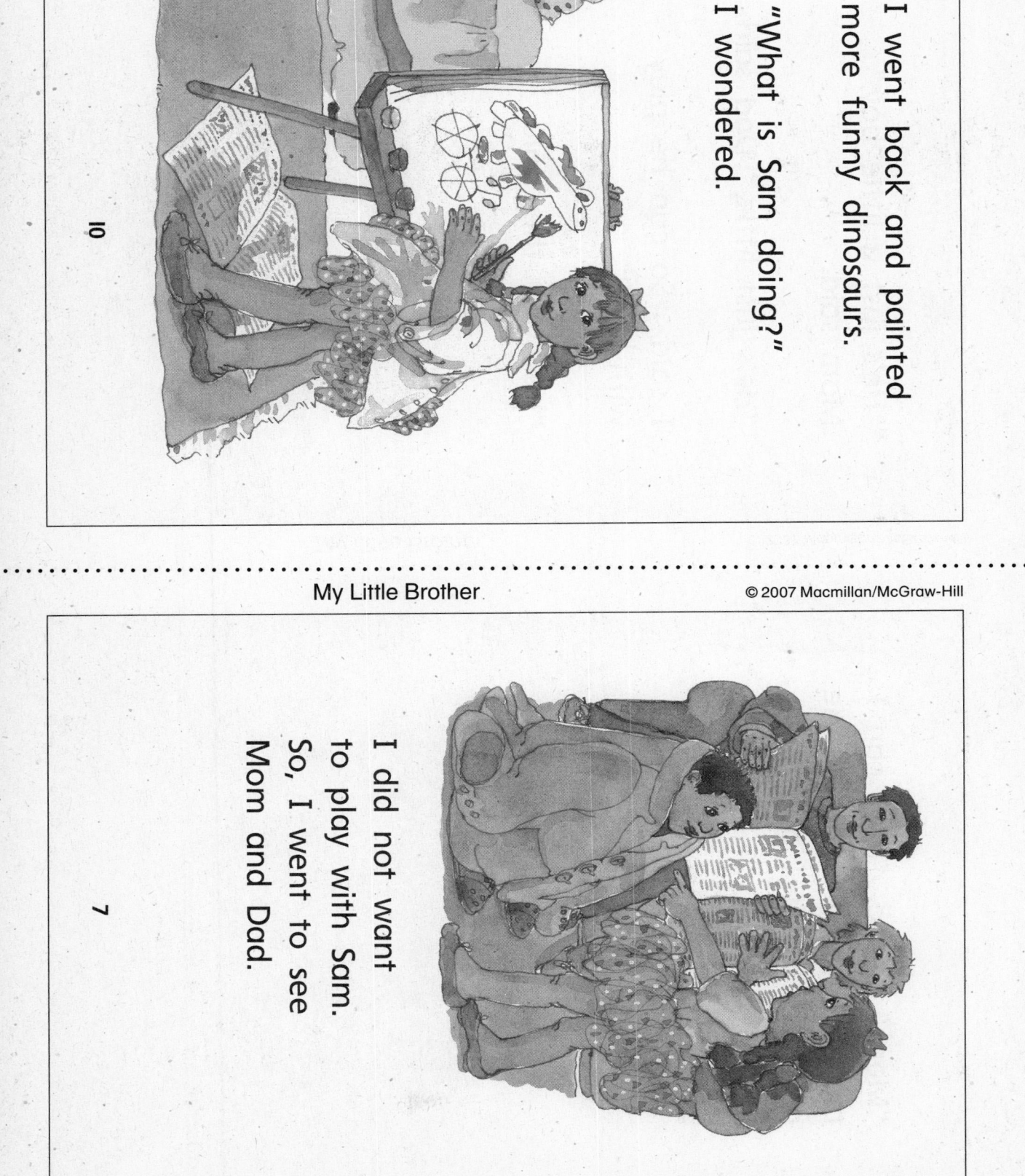

10

I did not want
to play with Sam.
So, I went to see
Mom and Dad.

7

8

"Mom," I said. "How can I play? Sam will not stop. He does just what I do."

9

"He's just a little boy," Mom said.

"He's just little," Dad said.

I said, "So can he play with you?"

"He can," they said.

Dear Family Member:

I'm reading *Gram and Me* this week. I'm learning about the characters in a story from how they act and what they say. In this story, the boy says things that let me know he likes his grandmother.

This Week's Skills

Comprehension: character and setting

Phonics: the sounds of scr, spl, and str

Spelling: words with scr, spl, and str

·····(fold here)·····

Word Workout

WORDS TO KNOW

give   were   say

about   read   says

Our Family Let's talk about our family using the words above.

MY SPELLING WORDS

scrap   scrub   splash

split   strike   string

Listening Time Repeat each word that I say. Stress the sounds the first three letters make. Now spell each word by writing it on my back.

Name _____

Who or Where?

Let's play a game! We'll write the numbers 1, 2, 3, and 4 on cards, and put the cards in a bag. We can use two coins or colored chips as markers. When it is your turn, pick a number from the bag and move that many spaces. Then tell if a character (who) or a setting (where or when) or both is pictured. Let's list how many characters and settings we land on. Whoever gets to the end first, wins.

Conexión con el hogar

Queridos familiares:

Estoy leyendo *Gram and Me* esta semana. Estoy aprendiendo acerca de los personajes en un cuento por cómo se comportan y por lo que dicen. En este cuento, un niño dice cosas que me dejan saber que a él le gusta su abuela.

Destrezas de la semana

Comprensión: personajes y ambiente

Fonética: los sonidos de scr, spl y str

Ortografía: palabras con scr, spl y str

·······(fold here)·······

© Macmillan/McGraw-Hill

Ejercicio de palabras

PALABRAS DE VOCABULARIO

give	were
about	say
read	says

Nuestra familia Hablemos acerca de nuestra familia usando las palabras de arriba.

PALABRAS DE ORTOGRAFÍA

scrap	scrub
split	splash
strike	string

Vamos a escuchar Repite cada palabra que digo. Acentúa los sonidos que hacen las primeras tres letras. Ahora, deletrea cada palabra escribiéndola con tu dedo en mi espalda.

Nombre _____

(225)

¿Quién o dónde?

¡Vamos a jugar! Vamos a escribir los números 1, 2, 3 y 4 en tarjetas y a colocarlas en una bolsa. Podemos usar dos monedas o dos fichas de colores como marcas. Cuando sea tu turno, escoge un número de la bolsa y mueve esa cantidad de espacios. Luego, di si aparece un personaje (quién) o un ambiente (dónde). Hagamos una lista para saber en cuántas casillas de personajes o ambientes hemos caído. Gana el primero que llegue a la biblioteca.

A Trip Last Spring

by Olivia Clay

illustrated by Deborah Melmon

This page is intentionally blank.

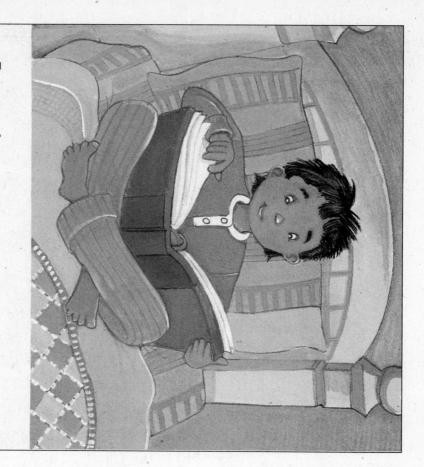

I am Jon.
I am looking at photos.
I think it is so much fun.

28

© 2007 Macmillan/McGraw-Hill

This page is intentionally blank.

Here I am with Mom and Dad. Last spring, we went on a plane to see Pop Streck. Pop Streck is Dad's dad.

A Trip Last Spring

There is much more to see. But it is time for bed. How can I save this spot? This string can save it!

This is Kim. Kim is five.
Kim has on a funny top.
It has stripes and dots!

A Trip Last Spring

This big, black dog is mine.
I call him Shag. Shag made
a splash in the mud.
I had to scrub him!

Talking with Grandpa

by Carlos Ramos

Comprehension Check

"I like to read," Grandpa says.

"I like to read, too," I say. "I am just like you, Grandpa!"

What the Characters Do	Where They Do It

Retell the Story

Use a Character and Setting Chart to help you retell the story.

Think and Compare

1. Where are the Grandpa and the boy sitting when they talk?

2. Name things you like to do.

3. How does this book show how

16

illustrated by Jeremy Tugeau

"Hi, Grandpa!" I say.

I give my Grandpa

2

"Wow! My wagon
looks just like that,"
I say.

15

a big hug.

"I'm looking at pictures," says Grandpa.

"Would you like me

3

Grandpa.

4

Talking with Grandpa

"This is me when I was little," says Grandpa.
"I liked to write stories on

to tell you about them?"

4

"This was my little red wagon," says Grandpa.

13

that typewriter."

"I like to write stories, too," I say. "I write them on

5

"And I like to talk on the phone to you,

12

my computer."

"Look at those skates,
Grandpa!" I say.

Grandpa says, "My skates

9

on the phone. I liked
to talk to my grandpa."

11

were strong and fast."

"I like to skate, too, Grandpa."

7

too," I say. "Tell me about another picture."

"Oh, look at this one," Grandpa says. "I am talking

10

I say. "Tell me
about another picture."

Grandpa says, "This is

8

my dad's car. My dad
liked to give me rides.

"That's funny. My dad
likes to give me rides,

9

Dear Family Member:

I'm reading *Pelican Was Hungry* in class. I'm learning that we can use story clues, picture clues, and what we already know to figure out things the author doesn't say. In this story, Pelican gets excited every time he sees something to eat. But nothing he sees is okay. I think Pelican is hungry.

This Week's Skills

Comprehension: make inferences

Vocabulary: words with more than one meaning

Phonics: the sound of **o** as in *home* and *pole*

Spelling: words with **o**

(fold here)

© Macmillan/McGraw-Hill

Word Workout

WORDS TO KNOW

every	any	saw	soon
opened	sparkled	floating	

Word Shuffle You can write down each word on small pieces of paper. I can shuffle them. Then I will hold a word up and you can say the word and use it in a sentence.

SPELLING WORDS

hose	joke	nose
note	vote	woke

Write It Right I'll say each word. Write each word on my back as you spell it aloud. How are all of these words alike?

Name _____

Figure It Out

We're going to use clues to fill in the crossword puzzle.

ACROSS

2. I am white and sweet to eat. I am a _____.

6. You can water the grass with me.
I am a _____.

7. I hold fish in my big beak. I am a _____.

9. I make you laugh. I am a _____.

DOWN

1. I live in the water and have a long nose.
I am a _____.

3. I am on your face. I am a _____.

4. I live in a shell. I am a _____.

5. I am a big, **big**, **big** sea animal. I am a _____.

8. A monkey is my relative. I am an _____.

Queridos familiares:

Estoy leyendo *Pelican Wa:*
Hungry en la clase. Estoy
aprendiendo que podemos
usar pistas del cuento, pistas
de los dibujos y lo que ya sab
para darnos cuenta de las co
el autor no dice. En este cuer
se pone contento cada vez qu
para comer. Pero nada de lo
bien. Pienso que Pelican ya d
hambriento.

Destrezas de la semana

Comprensión: hacer inferenc

Vocabulario: palabras con varios significados

Fonética: el sonido de **o** como en *home* y *pole*

Ortografía: palabras con **o**

(fold here)

© Macmillan/McGraw-Hill

Nombre _____

Ejercicio de palabras

PALABRAS DE VOCABULARIO

every	any	saw	soon
opened	sparkled	floating	

Baraja de palabras Puedes escribir cada palabra en
una hojita de papel. Puede barajarlas. Luego voy a derte
la palabra y puedes decirla y usarla en una oración.

PALABRAS DE ORTOGRAFÍA

hose	joke	nose
note	vote	woke

Escríbela correctamente Voy a decir cada palabra.
Escribe cada palabra con tu dedo sobre mi espalda
mientras la deletreas en voz alta. ¿En qué se parecen
todas estas palabras?

241

Resuélvelo

Vamos a usar pistas para completar el crucigrama.

ACROSS

2. I am white and sweet to eat. I am a _____

6. You can water the grass with me.
   I am a _____.

7. I hold fish in my big beak. I am a _____

9. I make you laugh. I am a _____.

DOWN

1. I live in the water and have a long nose.
   I am a _____.

3. I am on your face. I am a _____.

4. I live in a shell. I am a _____.

5. I am a big, **big**, **big** sea animal. I am a _____.

8. A monkey is my relative. I am an _____.

Mole Bakes at Home

by Tess Winter
illustrated by Emilie Boon

Mole Bakes at Home

This page is intentionally blank.

"Can you give me a ride to an apple grove?" asks Mole.
"I can not," says Fox.
So Mole rode his bike.

This page is intentionally blank.

Mole Bakes at Home

Mole chose about ten apples.
Those big apples were red!
Mole put his bag on a pole
and rode home.

3

Mole's nose woke him up.
Mole ate and ate.
"What can I say?" Mole
smiled. "It's the best!"

6

At home, Mole lit his stove.
"I will make a pie," he said.
"I will read and cut.
Then I will bake."

4

"I hope it tastes good,"
said Mole.
"I will put on a robe.
Then I will take a nap."

5

So Many Penguins

by Louise Tidd

Comprehension Check

Retell

Use the Make Inferences Chart to make an inference about the book.

What I Read	What I Know

→ Inference

Think and Compare

1. Look back at pages 12 and 13. What do you think the baby chick is saying to its mom?

2. Do you like penguins? Why or why not?

3. All animals need to eat. What else do penguins do that all animals do?

16

Penguins are birds that cannot fly. But every penguin can stand and walk on its little feet.

① Penguins live in large groups.

In this book, you saw many penguins. You saw where they live. Here are some more penguins. Where do you think these penguins live?

So Many Penguins

Penguins are very good swimmers. They have wings that help them swim. They have webbed feet that help them swim, too.

3

Soon it will be time for the penguins to go out to the open sea. They will stay there until it is time to make a nest.

14

This is the ⬆ biggest kind of penguin.

⬆ This kind of penguin is a very good hopper.

Look at some penguins. Are any penguins good hoppers?

4

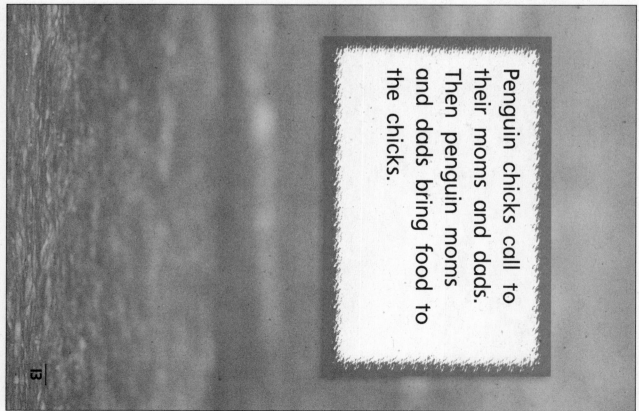

Penguin chicks call to their moms and dads. Then penguin moms and dads bring food to the chicks.

13

This kind of penguin has black feathers and a white front.

This kind of penguin has a bright red bill.

Do any penguins have red bills?

So Many Penguins

Penguins can dive. They dive
under the water to get food.

☉ These penguins are good divers.

9

☉ This baby chick has gray feathers.

Soon it will!
Penguin baby chicks do not
look like their moms and dads.
But, soon they will.

11

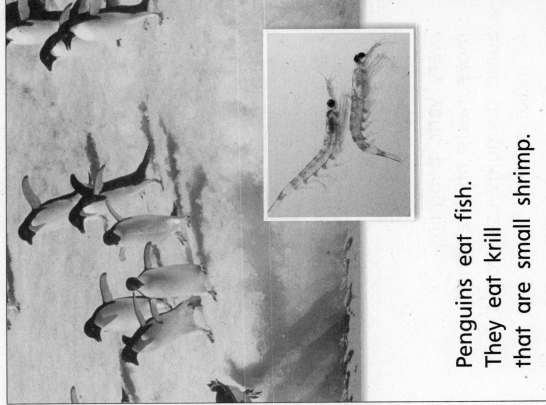

So Many Penguins

Penguins eat fish.
They eat krill
that are small shrimp.

This penguin warms the egg.

This penguin has an egg.
The penguin will keep
the egg warm.

When will the egg open?

Every year, penguins
make nests on the land.
Some penguins use stones
to make a nest.

This egg is in a nest made
of stones.

So Many Penguins

This nest is almost ready for an egg.

Some penguins make a hole.
They fill it with grass to make
a nest.

Dear Family Member:

I'm reading *June Robot Cleans Up* in class. June has a lot of junk. Her parents want her to get rid of it. I learned that we can put story clues and what we know from our own lives together. I understand that June and her parents have to agree. I wonder what June might make with the junk.

This Week's Skills

Comprehension: draw conclusions

Phonics: the sound of **u** as in *fuse*

Spelling: words with u_e

Name _____

······· (fold here) ·······

Word Workout

WORDS TO KNOW

| find | after | done | old |
| terrific | creation | new | work |

Story Time We're going to make up a story with these words. I'll ask you what each word means. Then we can make up a sentence using the word. We'll build a story with the sentences.

SPELLING WORDS

| cute | flute | June |
| mule | tune | use |

Crosswords Let's write a spelling word. Then we will write another word but write the letters from top to bottom. The letter **u** should connect the two words. Then we can try connecting other words with **u.**

255

Scared, Sad, or Glad

We're going to use what we know about emotions to help the robot better understand people. We'll do this by playing this game. Let's get two different coins. I'll write these sentences on cards and put them in a bag.

I'm scared.   I'm sad.   I'm glad.

• Put your coin on a **Begin** square.
• Pick a card from the bag.
• Move to the first space that matches the card.
• Put the card back in the bag.
• We'll take turns until one of us gets to the end.

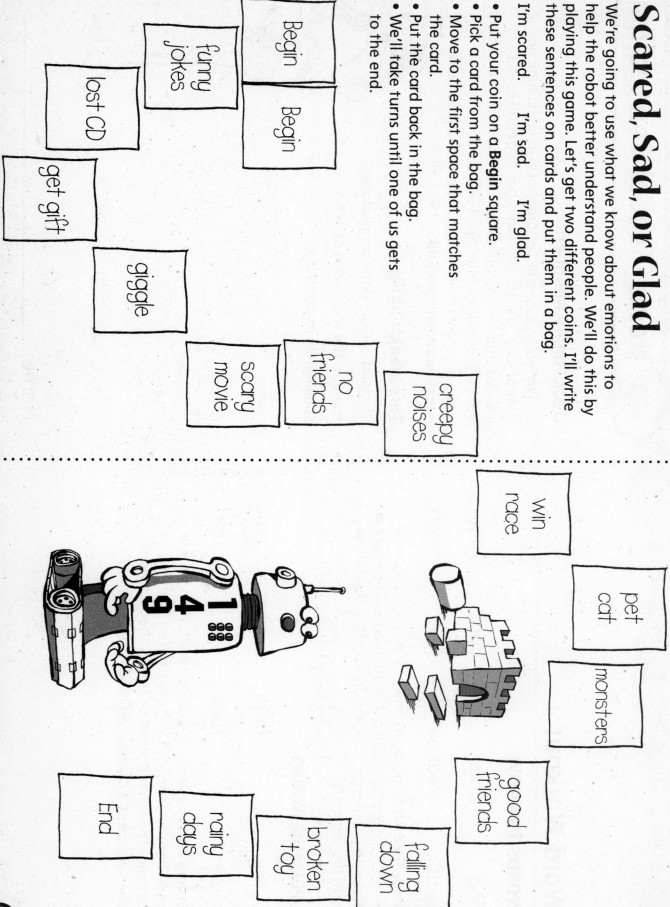

Begin

Begin

funny jokes

lost CD

get gift

giggle

scary movie

no friends

creepy noises

win race

pet cat

monsters

good friends

falling down

broken toy

rainy days

End

1
4
9

Conexión con el hogar

Queridos familiares:

Estoy leyendo *June Robot Cleans Up* en la clase. June tiene mucha chatarra y sus padres quieren que ella se deshaga de la chatarra. Aprendí que podemos poner las pistas del cuento junto con lo que sabemos a partir de nuestras propias experiencia Entiendo que June y sus padres tienen que estar de acuerdo. Me pregunto lo que June hará con la chatarra.

Destrezas de la semana

Comprensión: sacar conclusiones

Vocabulario: claves de contexto

Fonética: el sonido de u como en *fuse*

Ortografía: palabras con u_e

(Fold here)

Ejercicio de palabras

PALABRAS DE VOCABULARIO

find	after	done	old
terrific	creation	new	work

Tiempo de cuentos Vamos a inventar un cuento con tus palabras de vocabulario. Te voy a preguntar lo que cada palabra significa. Luego podemos escribir una oración usando la palabra. Vamos a armar un cuento con las oraciones.

PALABRAS DE ORTOGRAFÍA

cute	flute	June
mule	tune	use

Tiempo de crucigramas Escribe un par de palabras de ortografía, una horizontal y una vertical, usando en común la letra **u**. Escribe otros dos pares de palabras de la misma manera.

Nombre _____

Tiempo de aterrizar

Escribamos las siguientes oraciones en unas tarjetas y coloquémoslas en una bolsa. Vamos a usar dos monedas diferentes.

I'm funny.   I'm sad.   I'm glad.

- Coloca tu moneda en la casilla con la palabra Begin.
- Escoge una tarjeta de la bolsa.
- Avanza al primer espacio que tenga una palabra relacionada con la oración de la tarjeta.
- Coloca tu tarjeta de nuevo en la bolsa.
- Luego es mi turno. Tomaremos turnos hasta que uno de nosotros llegue al final del depósito de chatarra.

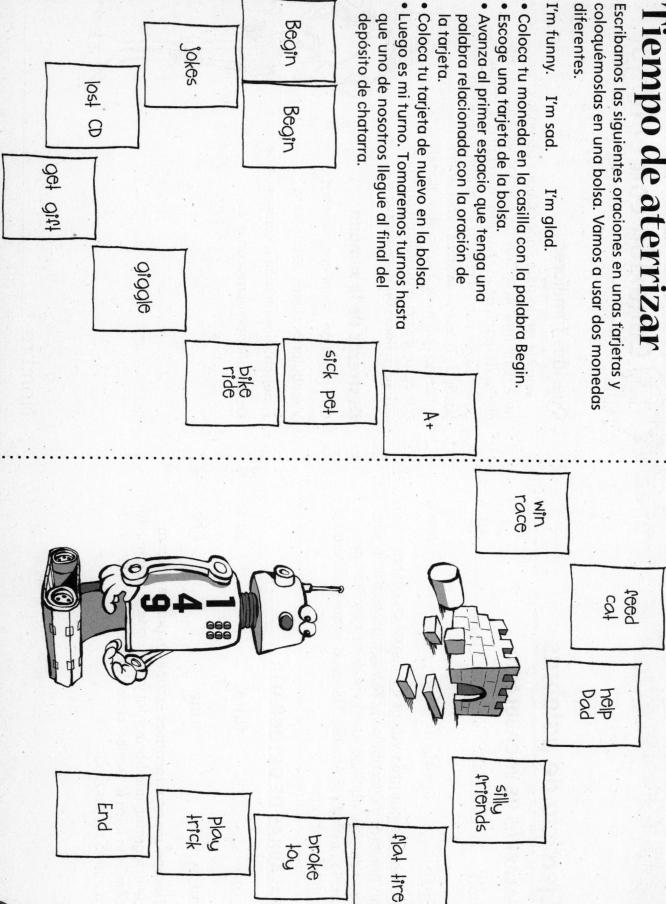

Begin   Begin

Jokes

lost CD

get gift

giggle

bike
ride

sick pet

A+

win
race

feed
cat

help
Dad

silly
friends

flat tire

broke
toy

Play
trick

End

Trash Rules!

by Carol Lindeen
illustrated by
Winifred Barnum-Newman

This page is intentionally blank.

I just saw this trash bin.
Soon it will spill over!
Can we cut back on trash?

8

This page is intentionally blank.

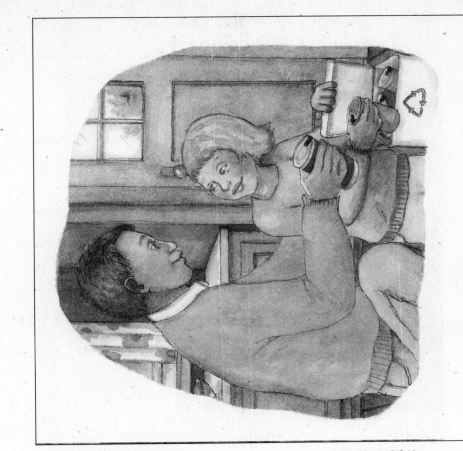

Can we spot any tin cans?
Toss them in that bin.

Trash Rules!

9

Let's use the best rules.
We can make less trash.

12

Let's save every big box.
Tape up the opened ends.
We can use them as blocks!

10

Let's use those tubes, too.
Tubes can make flutes.
Let's play a fun tune!

11

Save Paper Save Trees

by Nancy Jolson

Comprehension Check

Clue	Clue

Conclusion

Retell

Use a Draw Conclusions Chart to draw a conclusion about what you read.

Think and Compare

1. What happens to trees if people do not help to save paper?

2. This book tells how paper is recycled. What are some other things people can recycle? Do you think it is good to recycle? Why or why not?

3. This book tells how to help save trees. What other things in nature should people help to save?

16

Look around your school.
You will find lots
of things made of paper.

2

☞ Papier mâché is made with old newspapers, flour, and water.

Think about ways you can work to save paper.

- You can collect paper for recycling.
- You can use less paper.
- You can make new things from old things.

Save paper, save trees!

15

At home, you can find lots of things made of paper.

You can make something new from something old. Here is a terrific creation made from an old box.

◑ What kinds of paper products were used to make this?

Where does
all that paper
come from? Paper
is made from trees.
It takes many,
many trees to make
the paper people use.

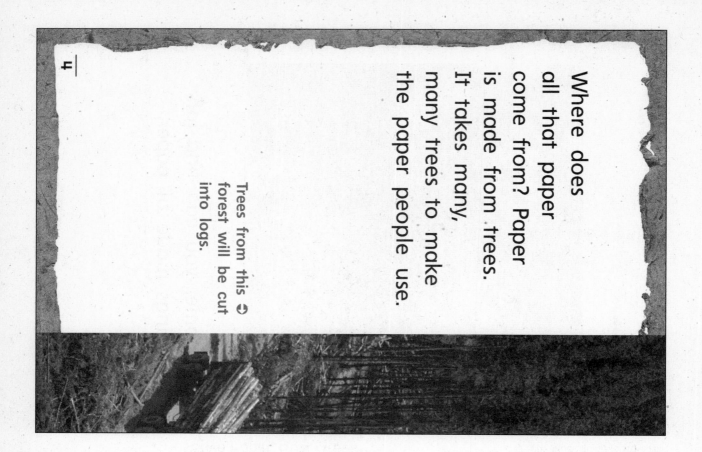

Trees from this ↻
forest will be cut
into logs.

4

Use paper shopping bags
more than one time.

13

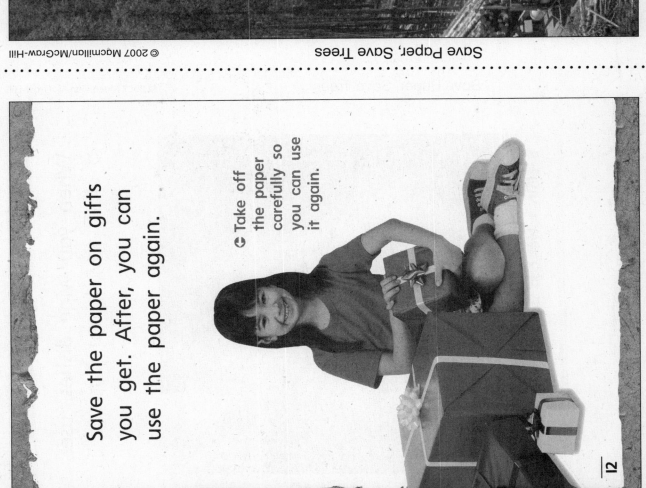

These logs will be sent to a paper mill and made into paper.

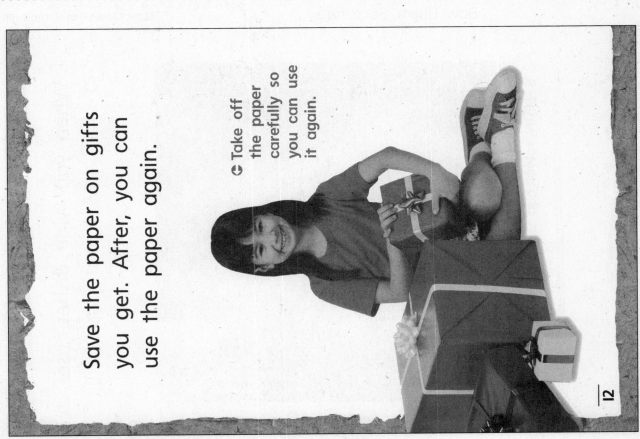

Save the paper on gifts you get. After, you can use the paper again.

Take off the paper carefully so you can use it again.

↻ This truck brings paper
to a recycling center.

How can people
help to save trees?
In some places, workers
collect paper for recycling.
Recycling is making
new things from old things.

Save Paper, Save Trees

When you wipe dishes, use
a cloth towel, not paper.

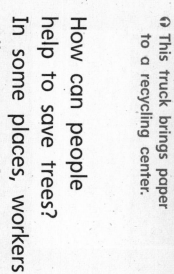

↻ A paper towel is thrown out, but
a cloth towel can be used again.

Sometimes people bring paper to a recycling center.

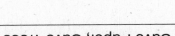

◑ People sort paper at a recycling center.

You saw how recycling old paper into new paper helps to save trees. You can help to save trees if you use less paper. After you are done with a paper, use the other side.

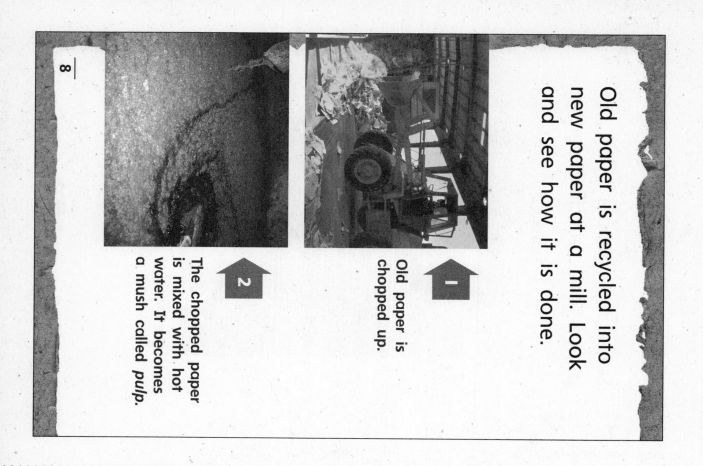

Old paper is recycled into new paper at a mill. Look and see how it is done.

1 Old paper is chopped up.

2 The chopped paper is mixed with hot water. It becomes a mush called *pulp*.

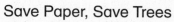

Save Paper, Save Trees

3 The pulp is cleaned. The water is pressed out.

4 The pulp is made into paper. The paper comes out in rolls.

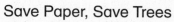

8

9

Home-School Connection

Dear Family Member:

I'm reading *Stormy Weather* in class. I'm learning to look for things that are alike and different. There are different kinds of storms. But all storms are alike in some ways. The sky turns gray when a storm is coming. There may be lightning and thunder during a rainstorm.

This Week's Skills

Comprehension: compare and contrast

Vocabulary: compound words

Phonics: the sound of ay and ai as in *way* and *tail*

Spelling: words with ay and ai

·······(fold here)·······

Name _____

Word Workout

WORDS TO KNOW

great	know	warm	sound
extreme	predict	cold	their

Sentence Time I'll say a sentence with a missing word. I'll say "blank" for the word. You can repeat the sentence using one of the words above for the missing word.

SPELLING WORDS

day   mail   play   rain   chain   way

Brain Play I'll read each word with you. Tell me if the sound you hear for the vowel or vowels in the word is the same as in the word *gray*. Can you tell me the letters that stand for the sound? Spell the word for me.

Rain, Rain, Go Away

It's a rainy day! Look at the clouds in the sky. Let's use gray to color all the clouds that are alike. Then color the rest of the clouds and the picture.

In the second picture, let's pick one kind of flower, then color all the flowers that are different.

Queridos familiares:

Estoy leyendo *Stormy Weather* en la clase. Estoy aprendiendo a buscar cosas que son parecidas y diferentes. Hay muchos tipos de tormentas. Pero todas las tormentas se parecen en algo. El cielo se torna gris cuando se acerca una tormenta. Puede haber relámpagos y truenos durante un temporal.

Destrezas de la semana

Comprensión: comparar y contrastar

Vocabulario: palabras compuestas

Fonética: el sonido de *ay* y *ai* como en *way* y *tail*

Ortografía: palabras con *ay* y *ai*

Nombre _____

Ejercicio de palabras

PALABRAS DE VOCABULARIO

great	know	warm	sound
extreme	predict	cold	their

Tiempo de oraciones Voy a decir una oración con una palabra que falta. Voy a decir la palabra *blank* en lugar de la palabra que debe ir. Repite la oración usando una de las palabras de arriba para la palabra que falta.

PALABRAS DE ORTOGRAFÍA

day	mail	play	rain	chain	way

Juego de cerebro Voy a leer cada palabra contigo. Dime si el sonido que escuchas para la vocal o las vocales es el mismo sonido que en la palabra *gray*. ¿Puedes decirme qué letras significa ese sonido? Deletréame la palabra.

Lluvia, lluvia vete

¡Hoy es un día de lluvia! Observa las nubes en el cielo. Usemos el color gris para colorear todas las nubes que son parecidas. Luego, vamos a colorear las otras nubes y el resto del dibujo.

En el segundo dibujo, vamos a elegir una flor y a colorear todas las flores que son diferentes a esa flor.

Too Much Rain Today

by Doreen Beauregard

illustrated by Nancy Cote

Too Much Rain Today

This page is intentionally blank.

14

Rain is on Mom's gray rug!
Rain is in Mom's braid!
Rain is on Big Jay's tail!

This page is intentionally blank.

I find new pails.
I get old pails.
I work with Mom.
I catch a lot of rain.

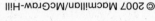

I see a big rainbow!
It makes us smile.
It's a fine day after all!

The rain is done!
May I run and play?
This yard has
too much mud!

16

Big Jay can't use
his house.
Big Jay sits and waits.

17

What Will the Weather Be?

by Nancy Leber

Comprehension Check

Retell

Look back at the pictures in this book. Use them to retell to a partner what you learned about weather.

Think and Compare

1. Look back at the book. How is the weather on Sunday and Monday the same? How is it different?

2. Reread about the weather on Tuesday. Pretend your weather is like that today. What will you do today? What will you wear?

3. Why do people want to know the weather ahead of time?

16

Find Florida on the map.
Find Miami (★) on the map.

2

Thursday	Friday	Saturday	Sunday

The weather changes from day to day. What will the weather be where you live?

15

Let's look at the weather
in Miami, Florida.

What will the weather be?

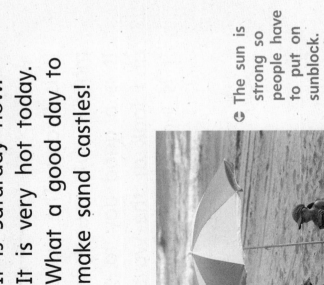

What Will the Weather Be?

Sunday	Monday	Tuesday	Wednesday

It is Saturday now.
It is very hot today.
What a good day to
make sand castles!

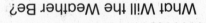 The sun is
strong so
people have
to put on
sunblock.

Sunday	Monday	Tuesday	Wednesday

It is Sunday. People on TV predict the weather. They let you know Sunday will be a hot, sunny day.

What Will the Weather Be?

Thursday	Friday	Saturday	Sunday

It is Friday. The waves make a soft sound now. It is a good day to sit and look at the waves. It is warm and sunny.

There are no big waves and no wind.

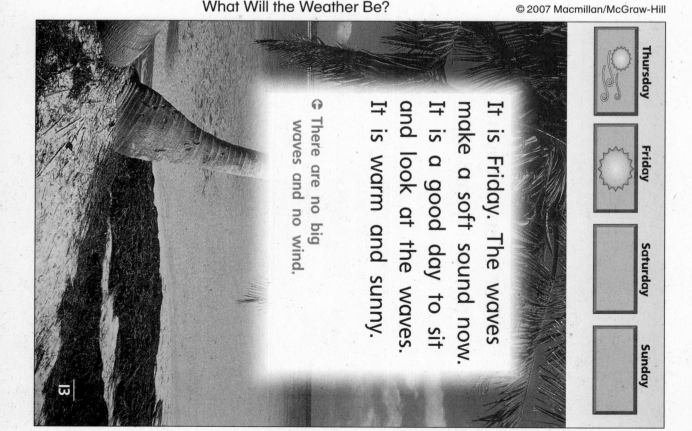

13

Thursday | Friday | Saturday | Sunday

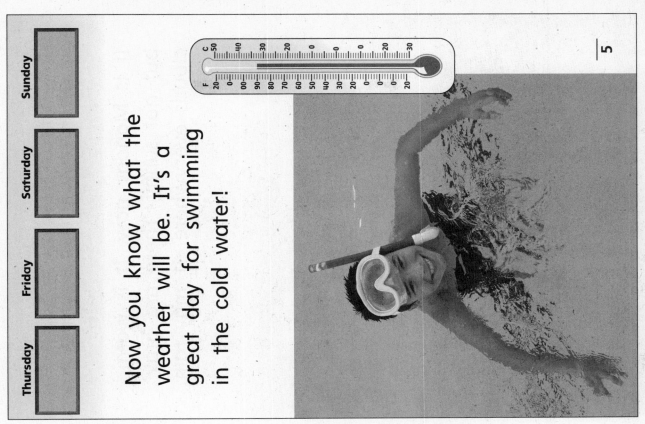

Now you know what the weather will be. It's a great day for swimming in the cold water!

What Will the Weather Be?

Sunday | Monday | Tuesday | Wednesday

Sunday	Monday	Tuesday	Wednesday

It is Monday now. It is warm, but not sunny. There are gray clouds everywhere. It may rain.

9

Thursday	Friday	Saturday	Sunday

This weather vane shows which direction the wind is blowing.

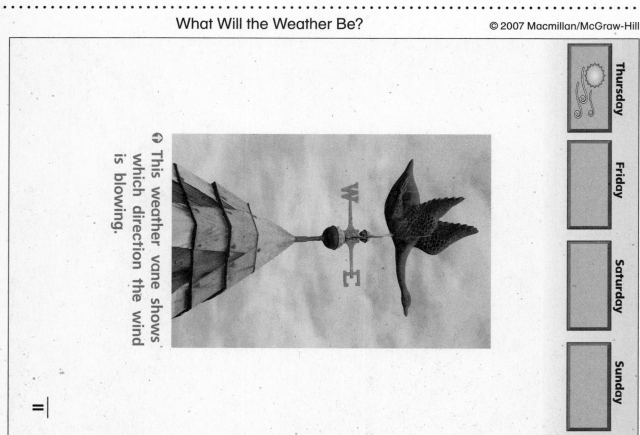

11

Thursday | Friday | Saturday | Sunday

These girls dressed for rain. They have raincoats and umbrellas.

It is Tuesday now. It is a rainy, wet day. People will have to use their umbrellas.

7

Sunday | Monday | Tuesday | Wednesday

It is Thursday now. It is sunny and windy, too.

The boy and girl think it is a good day to fly their kites.

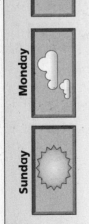

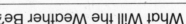

The wind lifts the kite into the air.

10

Sunday	Monday	Tuesday	Wednesday

Waves are higher when the wind is strong.

It is Wednesday now. A great big rainstorm is here. It is windy and wet. The rain is cold.

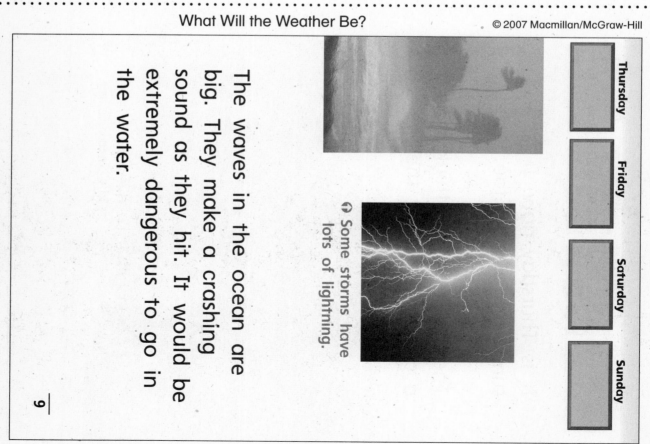

Thursday	Friday	Saturday	Sunday

Some storms have lots of lightning.

The waves in the ocean are big. They make a crashing sound as they hit. It would be extremely dangerous to go in the water.

Dear Family Member:

I'm reading Meet Ben Franklin in class. We reviewed how to make good guesses when we read. We can use story clues, picture clues, and what we already know. In this book, Ben was curious about lightning. He flew a kite with an iron key on the string and discovered electricity. I guess that Ben will do more with electricity because he is so curious. And Ben is smart!

This Week's Skills

Comprehension: make inferences

Phonics: the sounds of long e spelle ee, ea, e

Spelling: words with ee, ea, and e

Name _____

(fold here)

Word Workout

WORDS TO KNOW

knew	kind	house	friends
by	far	curious	idea

Map Making Let's draw a map of where your *friends* live. We can draw their *house* and add places that are close *by*. Then you can tell me about the map using the words.

SPELLING WORDS

beak	feed	keep
me	seat	we

Brainstorming Time Let's think of things in a kitchen that have the sound of long e as in *meet* or *be*. If you see it in the kitchen, I'll give you a sticky note to write its name. Then stick the note on the object.

Guess What Happens

Choose a picture. Tell
me what the person
is doing. Then guess
what will happen next.
On the next page, draw
a picture to show what
happens.

Conexión con el hogar

Querido familiares:

Estoy leyendo *Meet Ben Franklin* en la clase. Repasamos cómo hacer buenas predicciones cuando leemos. Podemos usar pistas del relato, pistas de los dibujos y las cosas que ya sabemos. En este libro, Ben estaba curioso acerca de los relámpagos. Hizo volar un papalote con una llave de hierro atada al hilo y descubrió la electricidad. Supongo que Ben va a hacer más cosas con la electricidad porque él es muy curioso. ¡Y Ben es muy listo!

Destrezas de la semana

Comprensión: hacer inferencias

Fonética: los sonidos de ee, ea y e

Ortografía: palabras con ee, ea y e

Nombre _____

(fold here)

Ejercicio de palabras

PALABRAS DE VOCABULARIO

knew	kind	house	friends
by	far	curious	idea

Haz un mapa Vamos a dibujar un mapa donde viven sus *friends*. Podemos dibujar su *house*, y añade lugares que son cerca *by*. Luego puedes decirme sobre el mapa y usas las palabras.

PALABRAS DE ORTOGRAFÍA

beak	feed	keep
me	seat	we

Lluvia de ideas Vamos a pensar en las cosas que hay en una cocina cuyos nombres tienen el sonido e larga como en las palabras *meet* o *be*. Si las ves en la cocina, te daré un papel autoadhesivo para escribir su nombre. Después, adhiere el papel autoadhesivo en el objeto.

Tres en raya

Vamos a jugar un juego de tres en raya. Observa el primer dibujo. Piensa por qué la persona está haciendo lo que muestra el dibujo. Luego, coloca una X o una O en el tablero del juego de tres en raya. Luego es mi turno. ¡Gana el primero que tenga tres en raya!

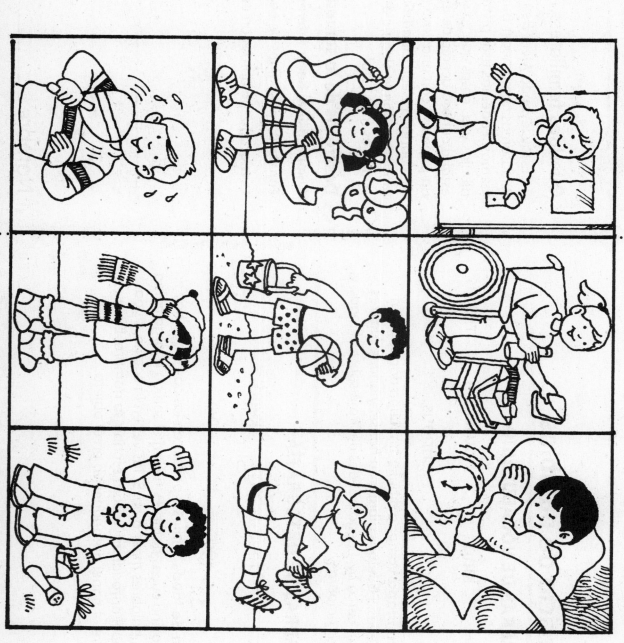

Feel the Heat

by Jay Howard

Is the meat done yet?
He peeks at the
thermometer to see.
Then he will eat his meal.

26

How do we know if it's hot?
How can we tell if it's cold?
This thermometer can
tell us.

Feel the Heat

It is hot, hot, hot!
The kids like to get
their feet wet.
It feels great!

We run fast and
breathe the cold air.
We need warm hats.
Then we will not freeze!

21

Feel the Heat

We are at the beach.
We like the waves.
We like the sound of
the sea.

24

She is sneezing a lot.
She has red cheeks.
Can she be sick? What can
Mom use to find out?

22

© 2007 Macmillan/McGraw-Hill

"Please stay in bed and
rest," Mom says.
She reads and sleeps.

23

Sylvia Earle
Scientist of the Sea

by Jeri Cipriano

Table of Contents

Comprehension Check

Retell

Use the Make Inferences Chart to make an inference about what you read.

What I Read	What I Know

→ Inference

Think and Compare

1. The book says that Sylvia was "curious." What other words can you use to tell what Sylvia was like? Tell why you think so.

2. Sylvia knew what she wanted to do when she grew up. What do you want to do? Why?

3. Do you think her work was interesting? Why or why not?

16

What Did Sylvia Study?

Sylvia Earle was a curious girl. For a time, she lived in a house by the sea. She would spend time by the shore. The sea became her friend.

Sylvia Earle Scientist of the Sea

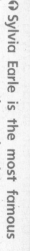

Sylvia Earle is the most famous woman marine scientist.

Sylvia always knew she had to share what she had seen. Sylvia wrote books to share her ideas about how to take care of our seas.

She wanted to know about all kinds of sea plants and animals. When she grew up, she would study life in the sea.

➊ The sea is filled with many kinds of living things. These are horseshoe crabs.

Sylvia Earle Scientist of the Sea

Sylvia Earle's Special Years A Time Line	
1970	She spent two weeks in a deep-sea lab.
1979	She set the world's record for deepest solo dive.
1984	She went down more than 3,000 ft. in Deep Rover.
1998	People named Sylvia a Hero for the Planet.

4

Sylvia learned to dive.
She put on a face mask
and a tank for breathing.
The tank gave her air.

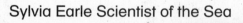
The mask and tank let
Sylvia stay underwater
for a long time.

This underwater sub is called Deep Rover.

Going down 1,250 feet was
amazing. But Sylvia knew she
wanted to go deeper. An
underwater sub like this one
took Sylvia down 3,000 feet!

13

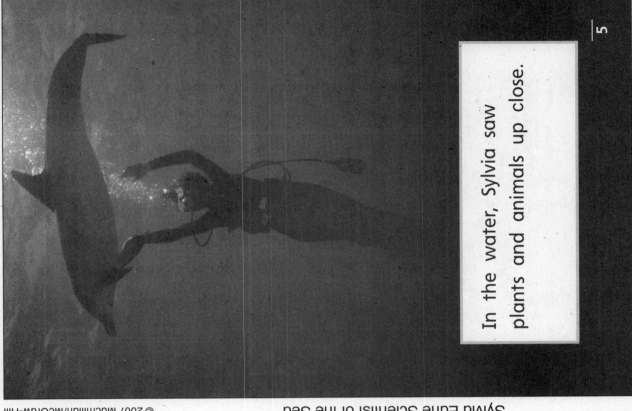

In the water, Sylvia saw plants and animals up close.

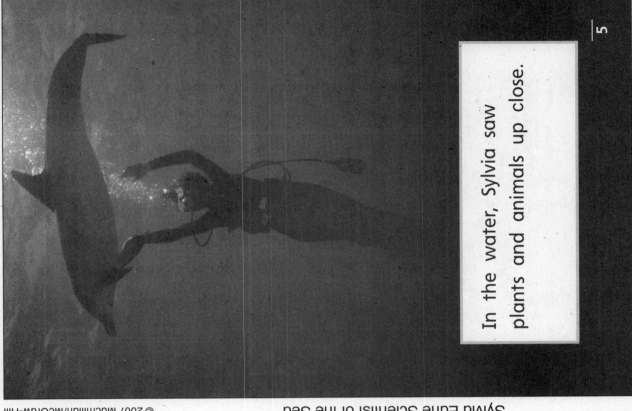

Sylvia Earle Scientist of the Sea

Sylvia walked on the sea floor. Like the men who walked on the moon, she had an American flag with her.

⊕ Sylvia holds the world's record for the deepest dives.

Where Did Sylvia Go?

Soon one of Sylvia's dreams came true. She would live under the water.

9

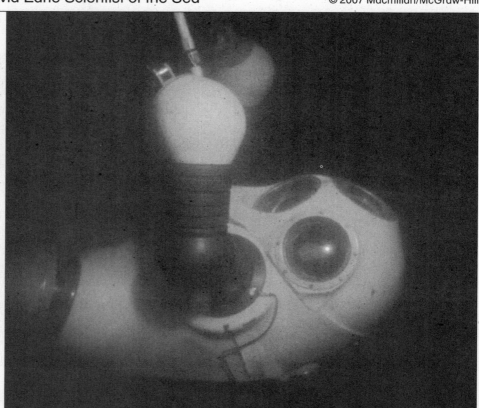

↷ Sylvia wore a special suit, called a Jim suit, for this trip. A strap kept her attached to the sub.

11

Sylvia and her friends had a special deep-sea lab. It was like having a house in the deep sea.

The team lived under the water for two weeks.

Sylvia Earle Scientist of the Sea

How Far Down Did Sylvia Dive?

Sylvia did something that no one had done before her. She went 1,250 feet down into the ocean. That's far!

This sub took Sylvia down into the water.

From the lab, Sylvia could swim out to explore the sea life. She collected many facts about all kinds of plants and animals.

8

Sylvia could spend lots of time exploring.

9

Dear Family Member:

I'm reading *Little Rabbit* in class. I learned that every story has a beginning, middle, and end. This story begins when Little Rabbit hears a thump. He thinks the forest is falling! I wonder how the story will end. I'm pretty sure the forest isn't falling.

This Week's Skills

Comprehension: beginning, middle, and end

Vocabulary: context clues

Phonics: the sound of long e as in *party* and *sunny*

Spelling: words that end in **y**

(fold here)

© Macmillan/McGraw-Hill

Word Workout

WORDS TO KNOW

heard	happen	fall	told
before	began	glared	haste

Art Time Draw any picture you want! Then tell me a story about the picture using the words.

MY SPELLING WORDS

bumpy	penny	puppy
sandy	funny	bunny

Listening Time Repeat each word that I say. Then say each word without the last sound. What letter stands for this sound in your spelling words? Now spell the word as you use your finger to write it on your leg.

Name _____

303

Make a Story

Color any picture in the Beginning row. I'll color a picture in the Middle row that tells the middle of the story. In the End row, we can finish the story and color it. Then we can start a new story with a new color.

Beginning

Middle

End

Queridos familiares:

Estoy leyendo *Little Rabbit* en la clase. Aprendí que cada cuento tiene un comienzo, un medio y un final.

Este cuento comienza cuando Little Rabbit escucha un golpe fuerte. ¡Él piensa que el bosque se está cayendo!

Me pregunto cómo terminará el cuento. Estoy casi seguro de que el bosque no se está cayendo.

Destrezas de la semana

Comprensión: comienzo, medio y final

Vocabulario: claves de contexto

Fonética: el sonido de e larga como en *party* y *sunny*

Ortografía: palabras que terminan en y

Nombre _____

(fold here)

© Macmillan/McGraw-Hill

Ejercicio de palabras

PALABRAS DE VOCABULARIO

heard	happen	fall	told
before	began	glared	haste

Vamos a dibujar ¡Haz un dibujo de alguna cosa quieres! Luego, dime un cuento sobre el dibujo y usas las palabras.

PALABRAS DE ORTOGRAFÍA

bumpy	penny	puppy
sandy	funny	bunny

Vamos a escuchar Repite cada palabra que digo. Luego, di cada palabra sin el último sonido. ¿Qué letra representa este sonido en tus palabras de ortografía? Ahora deletrea la palabra usando tu dedo para escribirla en tu pierna.

Haz un cuento

Colorea cualquier dibujo en la hilera donde dice BEGINNING. Yo voy a colorear un dibujo en la hilera donde dice MIDDLE que indica qué pasa en la mitad del cuento. En la hilera donde dice END, podemos terminar juntos el cuento y colorearlo. Luego, podemos comenzar un cuento nuevo con un color nuevo.

Beginning

Middle

End

Study the Trees

by Nancy Hardy

Study the Trees

This page is intentionally blank.

Let's study some trees.
Stop to see the trees
by many streets. Can you
name each kind you see?

28

This page is intentionally blank.

This is a pine tree.
I bet you knew that!
The cones can feel
bumpy and sticky.

29

Leave your house on a
sunny day.
Take a walk with friends.
Find out about trees!

32

When it gets chilly, each leaf on this tree gets red. Study a leaf up close. Pick it up. Take it home!

30

This tree bends far down. It sways when it's windy. If you feel sleepy, this is a fine spot for a nap.

31

The Lion and the Mouse

retold by *Cynthia Rothman*
illustrated by *Thomas Taylor*

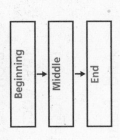

Table of Contents

Comprehension Check

Retell the Story

Use the Beginning, Middle, and End Chart to retell the story.

Beginning → Middle → End

Think and Compare

1. What problem did Mouse have at the beginning of the story? How did he solve it?

2. This book tells how Mouse and Lion became friends. Think about one of your friends. How did you become friends?

3. Mouse helped his friend Lion. How do people who are friends help each other?

16

Lion and Mouse Meet

One day Lion closed his eyes.
He wanted to fall asleep.

2

Lion was so happy. "Hop on my back," he said. "We will ride together."

And from that day to this, Lion and Mouse are still very good friends.

15

Then, Mouse came by.
Lion heard Mouse
and woke up.

3

The Lion and the Mouse

Before long, the hole
grew bigger and bigger.
And soon Lion was free.

4

Lion stretched out his paw.
He glared. Then he grabbed
the little mouse.

4

Mouse began to nibble at
the net. He made a little hole.

13

Mouse began to shake.
He didn't want to fall.

"Great Lion, let me go!"
said Mouse.

5

"You want to help, but you
are so little," Lion said.

"But I can help," said Mouse.
"Be still," he told Lion.

12

A Good Friend

"Why should I let you go?" asked Lion.

9

The Lion and the Mouse

Before long, Mouse saw what had happened. Lion was trapped in a big net.

"I will help you," Mouse told Lion.

11

Mouse said, "I am just
a little mouse. But I can
be a good friend to you."

7

Lion Needs Help

Days passed by. Then
one day Mouse heard
a great and terrible roar.

"Is that my friend?" Mouse
asked. "Did something happen
to Lion?"

Mouse ran in haste.

10

"How could a silly little mouse be a friend to me?" asked Lion.

"You will see," said Mouse.

"Ha! Ha! Ha!" said Lion. "Just go now. You made me happy today."

8

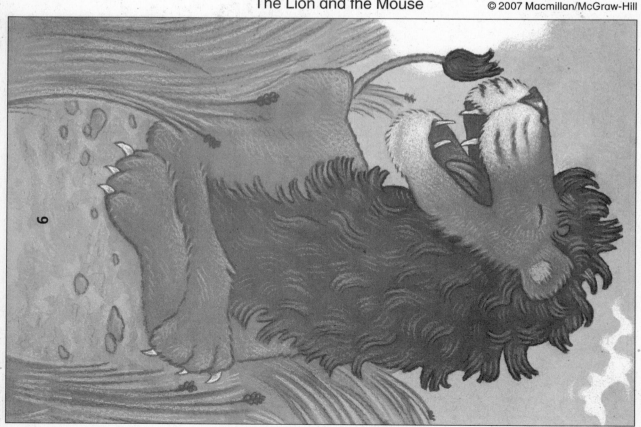

9

Dear Family Member:

I'm reading *Olivia* in class this week. Olivia does many of the same things that we do every day, but Olivia is a pig! I learned that stories can be fantasy or reality. Reality stories are about things that could really happen. A fantasy is a make-believe story that could not really happen.

This Week's Skills

Comprehension: fantasy and reality

Phonics: the sound of long **o** spelled **o**, **oa**, or **ow**

Spelling: words with **o**, **oa**, and **ow**

·········(fold here)·········

Word Workout

WORDS TO KNOW

mother	father	try	always
love	firm	supposed	

Sentence Time I'll say a sentence for each of the words, but I'll say "blank" instead of the word. You can say the sentence back to me with the missing word.

SPELLING WORDS

boat	coat	go
low	no	row

Sort the Words Fold a piece of paper in half. Write **boat** on one side and **go** on the other side. Now I'm going to ask you to spell the other words. Write each word below the word it rhymes with.

Name _____

Get Real

Let's play a game! We'll need two small objects for markers.

- Flip a coin. Move one space for heads or two spaces for tails.
- Look at the picture in the box you land on. Tell if the picture shows a fantasy or reality.
- We'll take turns. Whoever gets to the museum first, wins!

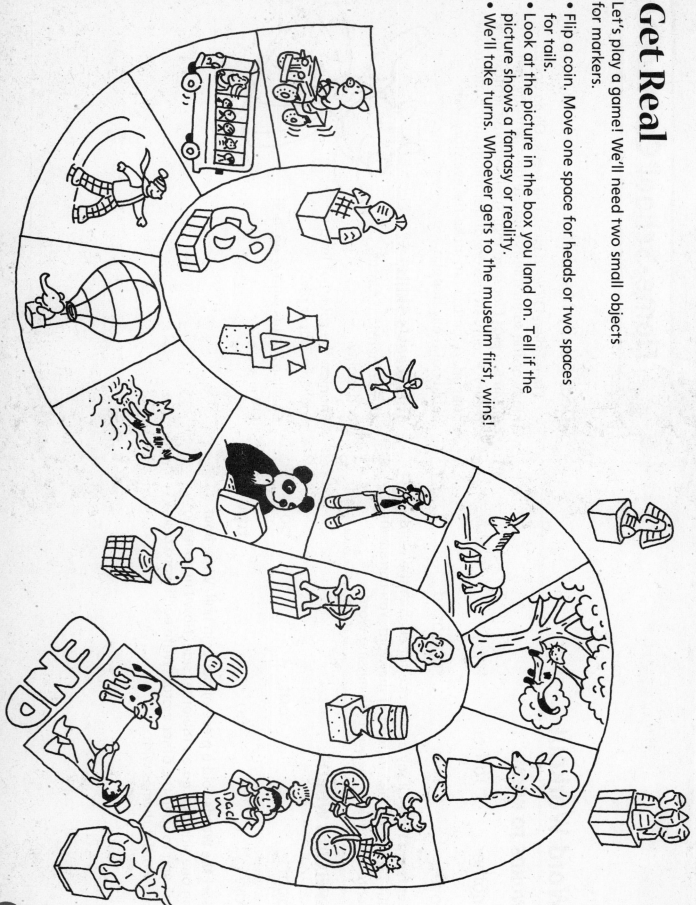

Queridos familiares:

Estoy leyendo *Olivia* en la clase esta semana. Olivia hace muchas de las mismas cosas que nosotros hacemos todos los días. ¡Pero Olivia es una cerdita!

Aprendí que los cuentos pueden ser relatos de fantasía o realistas. Los cuentos realistas son acerca de cosas que realmente podrían ocurrir. Un cuento de fantasía es un relato fantasioso que no podría ocurrir en la realidad.

Destrezas de la semana

Comprensión: fantasía y realidad

Fonética: los sonidos de **o** larga deletrea **o, oa,** o **ow**

Ortografía: palabras con **o, oa,** y **ow**

Ejercicio de palabras

PALABRAS DE VOCABULARIO

mother	father	try	always
love	firm	supposed	

Tiempo de oraciones Voy a decir una oración para cada una de las palabras, pero diré la palabra *blank* en lugar de la palabra que debería ir allí. Dime la oración de nuevo completándola con la palabra que falta.

PALABRAS DE ORTOGRAFÍA

boat	coat	go
low	no	row

Clasifica las palabras Dobla una hoja de papel a la mitad. Escribe la palabra **boat** en un lado y la palabra **go** en el otro lado. Ahora te voy a pedir que deletrees las otras palabras. Escribe cada palabra debajo de la palabra con la que rima.

Nombre _____

Sé realista

¡Vamos a jugar un juego! ¡Vamos a necesitar dos objetos pequeños para usar como fichas.

- Tira una moneda. Avanza un espacio si sale *heads* o dos espacios si sale *tails*.
- Observa la ilustración en la casilla en la que caes. Di si la ilustración tiene un personaje fantasioso o realista.
- Vamos a tomar turnos. ¡Gana el primero que llega al museo!

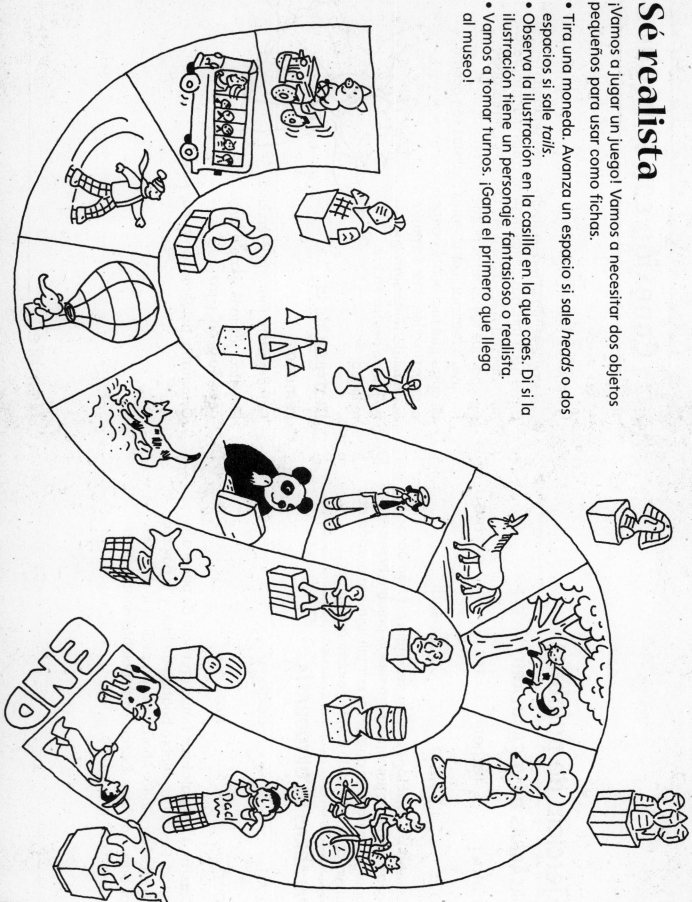

Be Bold and Show It!

by Lucy McCloud

This page is intentionally blank.

Have you heard? Making things can be fun.
You can use paint and clay.
You can use sand and snow.
Let's see what these kids made!

2

This page is intentionally blank.

Snow fell, but no one told Jim
it's too cold to play!
His coat is keeping him toasty!
Jim made a snowman!

Be Bold and Show It!

So get set and make things!
Be bold and show the things
you make.
People will think you are a pro!

6

These kids made a sand castle.
The kids piled up sand
and patted it.
Go get Mom before the waves
come up and it falls!

4

These kids began with a lump
of clay. Get hold of some clay
and mold it. What can happen?
You can make a bowl, a boat,
or a snake!

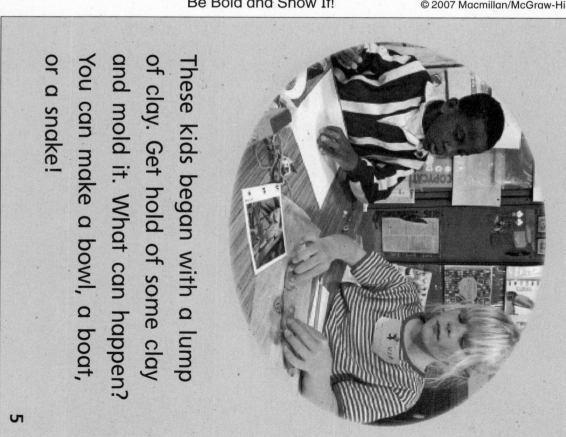

5

The Painting

by Rosie Mackie
illustrated by David Sheldon

Table of Contents

Comprehension Check

Retell the Story

Use a Fantasy and Reality Chart to help you tell what happened in the story.

What Happens	Why It Could Not Happen in Real Life
1	1
2	2
3	3

Think and Compare

1. Look back at page 5. Why did Mike like that picture so much?

2. What school trip did you find exciting? Why?

3. Why do you think people like to look at art?

16

At the Art Gallery

Mike's class was at the art gallery. "Always stay together, class," said Mrs. West. "We don't want anyone to get lost."

The Painting

Mike told Zack all about rowing the boat in the painting. Zack supposed that Mike was just making up a story.

What do you think?

The Painting

Just then Mike heard Zack say,
"Come on Mike. Let's go.
There are more paintings to
look at. Why did you look at
this painting for so long?"

"Wait until I tell you what
happened," said Mike.

14

The children stopped in one room. There were many paintings to see.

"Come look at this one, Zack," said Mike.

Mike looked at the painting. There were people rowing boats on a lake. The sun was shining on the water.

4

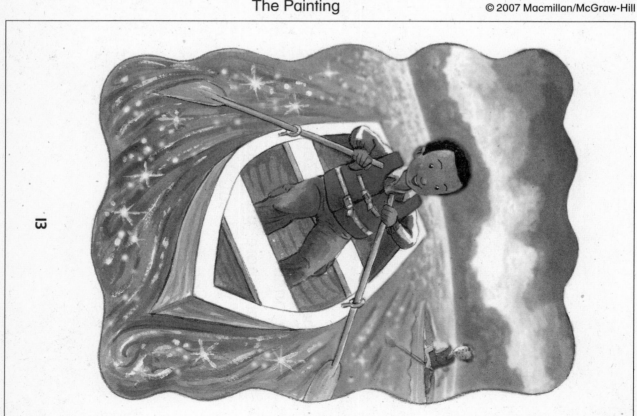

13

The Painting

5

Mike put the oars in
the water and pulled.
His grip was firm. He
went for the ride of
his life.

Mike sailed past the
other boats. He wished
his mother and father
could see him.

12

Mike saw that one boat had no one in it. Mike loved boats.

"I wish I could be in that boat," Mike said. "I could be happy spending the day there."

6

Mike wanted to try to row the boat. His father had shown him how to hold the oars. His mother had shown him how to pull the oars. Now, it was time for Mike to try!

11

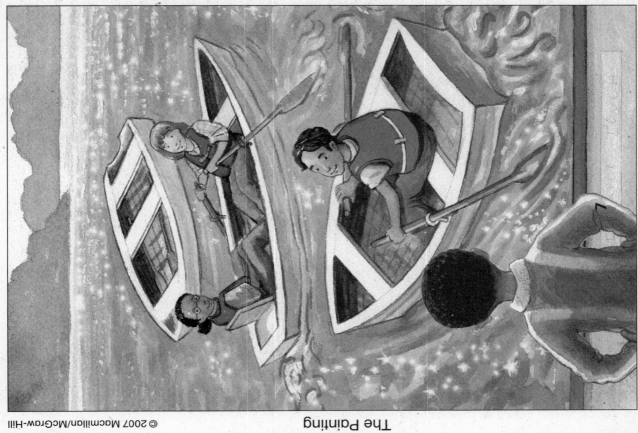

The Painting

The sunlight made the water sparkle. Mike felt so happy. He loved being in the painting.

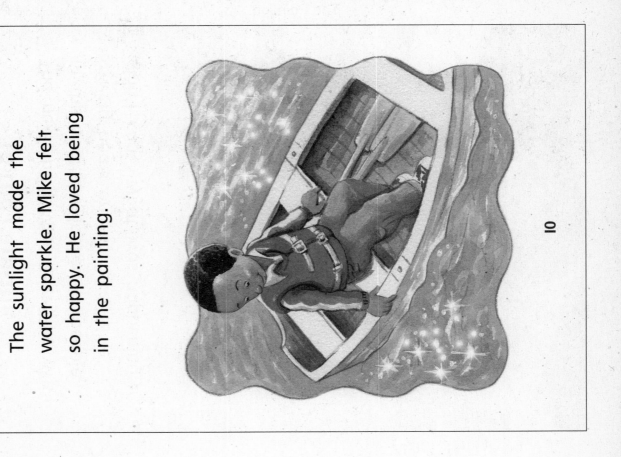

10

8

The Painting

© 2007 Macmillan/McGraw-Hill

9

In the Painting

The next thing Mike knew, he was in the boat! He looked at people rowing boats on the lake. Mike didn't know what was happening.

Home-School Connection

Dear Family Member:

I'm reading *The Kite* in class this week. I learned that most stories begin with a problem and end with a solution. This story begins with Toad trying to get his kite up in the sky. I guess that's the problem. Frog tells him something he can do to make the kite fly. Will that be the solution?

This Week's Skills

Comprehension: problem and solution

Phonics: sounds of long i spelled i, y, igh

Spelling: words with i, igh, and y

····················(fold here)····················

Name _____

Word Workout

WORDS TO KNOW

ball	shout	should	head	never
perhaps	laughter	meadow		

Story Time We're going to make up a story with the words. I'll ask you what each word means. Then we can make up a sentence using the word. We'll build a story with the sentences.

SPELLING WORDS

find	by	kind
my	night	right

Rhyme Time I'm going to ask you to spell each word. If the word has the same vowel sound as the word *try*, say a word that rhymes.

Jumpy Jumps Away

We're going to find out what happens to Jumpy. Let's talk about the pictures to see what problem Jumpy has. Then we can talk about the best way for Jumpy to solve his problem.

1. Jumpy goes for a walk.

2. Jumpy hops to the trees.

3. Jumpy is lost. "What will I do?"

4. What is the best way for Jumpy to solve his problem? Circle the letter or write your own idea.

a. Jumpy can follow a bird flying in the sky.

b. Jumpy can follow his own paw prints back home.

c. Jumpy can shout and hope someone comes to help him.

d. _____

5. Jumpy is back home.

Conexión con el hogar

Queridos familiares:

Estoy leyendo *The Kite* en la clase esta semana. Aprendí que la mayoría de los cuentos comienzan con un problema y terminan con una solución. Este cuento comienza con Toad tratando de remontar su papalote en el cielo. Supongo que ése es el problema. Frog le dice algo que él puede hacer para que el papalote vuele. ¿Será ésa la solución?

Destrezas de la semana

Comprensión: problema y solución

Fonética: los sonidos de i largo deletrea i, y, igh

Ortografía: palabras con i, igh e y

(told here)

Nombre _____

Ejercicio de palabras

PALABRAS DE VOCABULARIO

ball	shout	should	head
never	perhaps	laughter	meadow

Tiempo de cuentos Vamos a inventar un cuento con las palabras. Te voy a preguntar el significado de cada palabra. Luego, podemos inventar una oración usando la palabra. Vamos a armar un cuento con las oraciones.

PALABRAS DE ORTOGRAFÍA

find	by	kind
my	night	right

Vamos a rimar Te voy a pedir que deletrees cada palabra. Si la palabra tiene el mismo sonido de vocal como en *try*, entonces di una palabra que rime.

Jumpy se va brincando

Vamos a averiguar qué le pasa a Jumpy. Hablemos acerca de los dibujos para ver qué problema tiene Jumpy. ¿Cómo piensas que Jumpy resuelve el problema?

1. Jumpy goes for a walk.

2. Jumpy hops through the trees.

3. Jumpy is lost. What will Jumpy do?

4. Jumpy sees birds in the sky.

5. Jumpy follows one bird home.

6. Jumpy is happy.

What is Jumpy's problem?

How does Jumpy solve the problem?

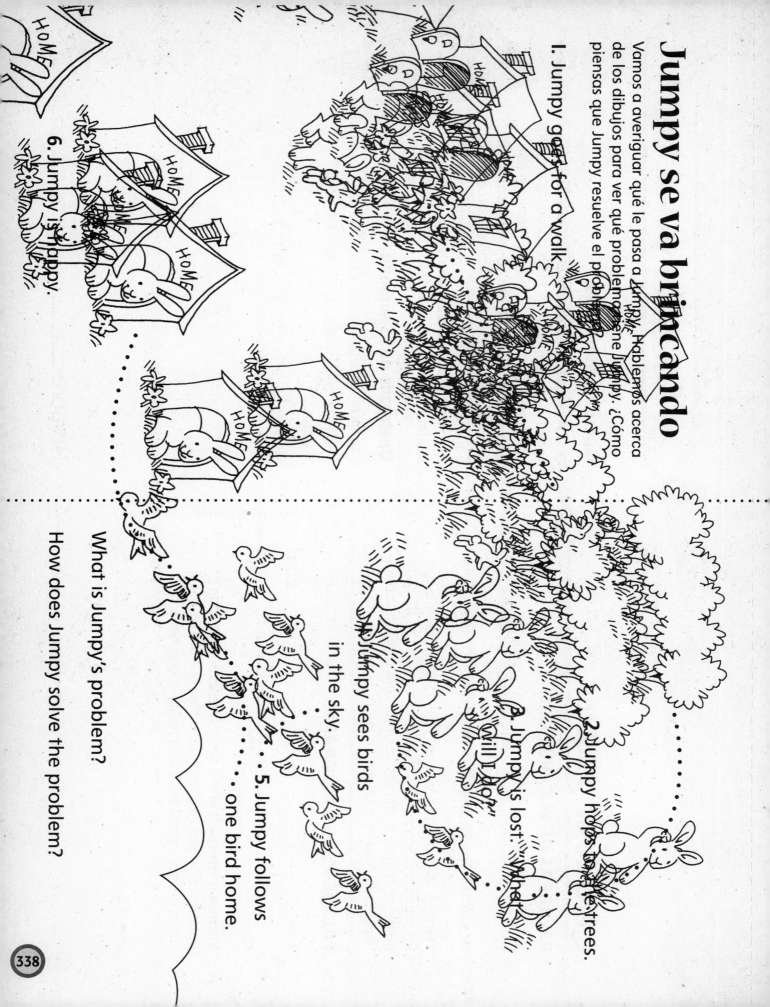

Flying High!

by Sherry Night

This page is intentionally blank.

People love to fly!
They do not mind being
high in the sky!
They find it's fun.

8

This page is intentionally blank.

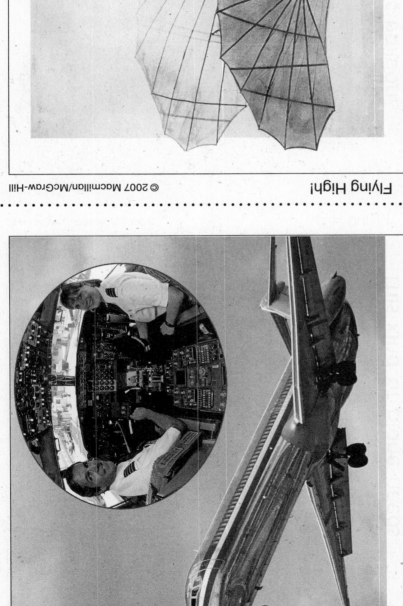

A man made a big kite.
He strapped it on tight.
Then he jumped from up high!
Did he fly? Yes, he did!

Flying High!

This plane is a jet.
A child can't fly it.
But a mother and father can.
Sit tight. It can go fast!

12

People can fly in this balloon.
Hot air makes it rise.
This wild ride is quite
a sight!
Try it one day.

10

This kind of plane needs
no gas. It floats on air.
It must always fly when
it's bright and sunny.
It has no lights!

11

Push and Pull

by Ellen Catala

illustrated by Hideko Takahashi

Table of Contents

Comprehension Check

Retell the Story

Use a Problem and Solution Chart to help you retell the story.

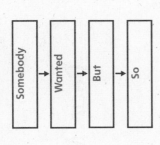

Somebody → Wanted → But → So

Think and Compare

1. Look back at page 12. How did Nick solve his problem of moving the box?

2. What is the best gift you ever were given? Why did you like it?

3. Do you think everyone likes to get gifts? Why or why not?

16

Something for Nick

Nick and Grandpa made a list of how things move.

2

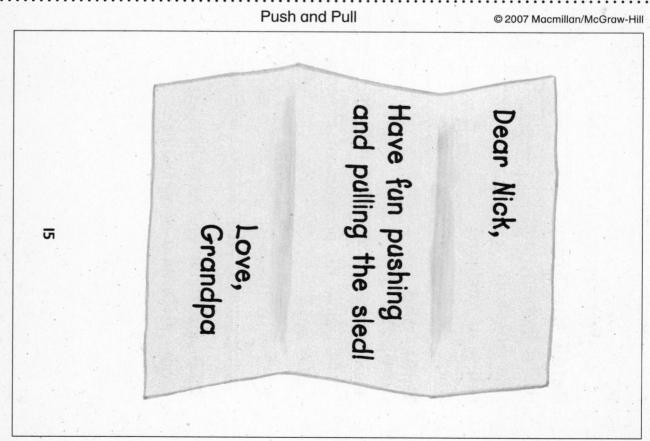

Dear Nick,

Have fun pushing and pulling the sled!

Love,
Grandpa

15

How Things Move

Things We Pull

wagon

kite string

curtain string

Things We Push

swing

piano keys

swinging door

Then Grandpa said, "I will send you a gift, Nick. It will be something to push or pull."

Push and Pull

3

Nick opened the box. Would the gift be something to push or pull? He saw a big, yellow sled and a ball for Sky. There was a letter from Grandpa, too.

4

Waiting for the Gift

Now Nick sat with his dog Sky. Nick was waiting for the mail.

"My gift should come today," he said. "Perhaps it will."

4

Just then flakes of snow fell. Nick and Sky woke up.

"The box is here," shouted Nick. "And it's not as big as in my dream!"

13

As he waited, Nick saw a bird.
"Look! The bird can pull the string from its nest," said Nick.

5

"I can not do this myself.
I need you, Sky," said Nick.
"This box needs a push and a pull."

Nick and Sky worked together.

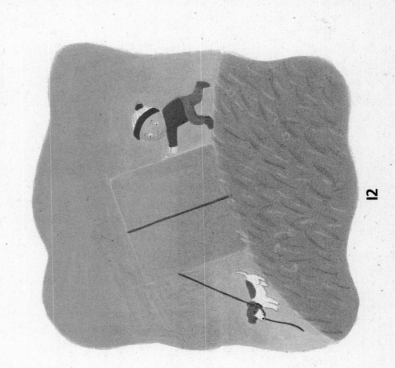

12

Then Nick saw a kitten.
"The kitten can push the ball,"
said Nick.

6

"So I will try to push it,"
Nick said. "Perhaps I should try
to pull it, too?"

But the box never moved. Nick
was little and the box was
so big.

11

Nick saw his mom at the front door.

"I saw a bird and a kitten pull and push. Grandpa was right," Nick said.

"That box is for me," Nick shouted. "I can take it now."

Gus went on his way.

Sky looked at the big, big box. "You will never lift that box," Sky said.

The Dream

Nick rested his head. Sky put his head down, too. They fell fast asleep. Nick dreamed he heard laughter. It was Gus with the mail.

8

Nick and Sky ran to a great, green meadow. Gus had a very big box.

9

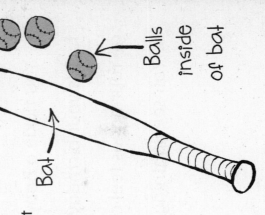

Top

Balls inside of bat

Bat

Dear Family Member:

I'm reading "Kids' Inventions" in class this week. In this article, children see things that make them invent things. What they see causes them to come up with something brand new. This is called *cause and effect*. I wonder what other inventions I'm going to read about this week.

This Week's Skills

Comprehension: cause and effect

Phonics: the sound of *ar* in arm

Spelling: words with *ar*

·····(fold here)·····

© Macmillan/McGraw-Hill

Word Workout

WORDS TO KNOW

| better | children | discovery | or |
| machine | round | | |

Use Clues I'm going to give you clues. You tell me which word above matches the clues.

| young | people | good | a shape |
| this ____ that | computer | find | |

SPELLING WORDS

arm   art   barn   cart   harm   yarn

Crossword Time We can write one spelling word and cross it with another spelling word.

h		
a	r	m
r		
m		

Let's try two more words. We can try all sorts of words.

Name _____

Matching Game

Let's read each cause below. Then let's look for its effect on the next page. Write the letter of the cause in front of its effect.

a. The phone rings.

b. Your pencil point breaks.

c. A cup of ice sits in the sun.

d. You can't hear the TV.

e. You tickle a baby.

f. It's your birthday.

g. Your hands feel cold.

h. You see lightning in the sky.

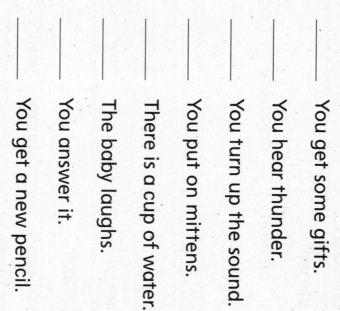

_____ You get some gifts.

_____ You hear thunder.

_____ You turn up the sound.

_____ You put on mittens.

_____ There is a cup of water.

_____ The baby laughs.

_____ You answer it.

_____ You get a new pencil.

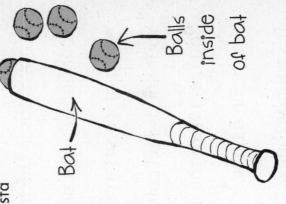

Queridos familiares:

Estoy leyendo *Kids' Inventions* en la clase esta semana. En este artículo, los niños ven cosas que les hacen inventar cosas. Lo que ven causa que se les ocurra algo completamente nuevo. A esto se le llama *causa y efecto*. Me pregunto acerca de qué otros inventos voy a leer esta semana.

Destrezas de la semana

Comprensión: causa y efecto

Fonética: el sonido de ar como en arm

Ortografía: palabras con ar

Top

Bat

Balls inside of bat

·······(fold here)·······

© Macmillan/McGraw-Hill

Nombre _____

Ejercicio de palabras

PALABRAS DE VOCABULARIO

better   children   discovery   or

machine   round

Usar pistas Te voy a dar pistas. Tú me dices qué palabra de arriba corresponde a las pistas que te doy.

young people   good   a shape

this ___ that   computer   find

PALABRAS DE ORTOGRAFÍA

arm   art   barn   cart   harm   yarn

Tiempo de crucigramas Vamos a escribir una palabra de ortografía y cruzarla con otra palabra de ortografía.

h		
a	r	m
a		
m		

Tratemos de hacerlo con dos palabras más. Usemos cualquier clase de palabras.

353

Punto a punto

Leamos las causas que aparecen aquí abajo. Tú comienzas primero. Dime lo que piensas que va a ocurrir. Con un creyón de color rojo, conecta dos puntos. Ahora es mi turno y conecto dos puntos con un creyón de color azul. Cuando formes un cuadrado, dibuja una **X** roja sobre el mismo. Vamos a seguir tomando turnos. Cuando todos los puntos estén conectados, gana el que tenga la mayor cantidad de cuadrados.

The phone rings.

A boy steps in the mud.

Your pencil point breaks.

A cup of ice sits in the sun.

Your hands feel cold.

You can't hear the TV.

You tickle a baby.

It's your birthday.

There is a knock at the door.

You see lightning in the sky.

Carly in the Dark

by Judith Bartley

illustrated by Alli Siena

This page is intentionally blank.

My name is Carly.
I'm a smart kid.
But I do NOT like the dark.
I know it will never harm me.
But I do NOT like the dark.

14

This page is intentionally blank.

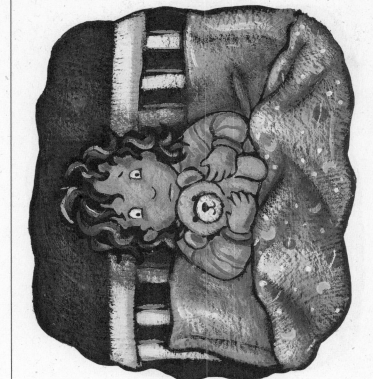

I try to sleep in the dark.
Mom says that I should.
But it's so hard!
I do NOT like the dark.

Carly in the Dark

Mom got me a night-light.
She's so smart!
Now I can sleep.
I'm a "sleeping star"!

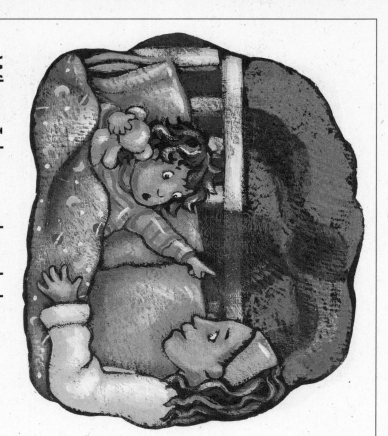

When I lay my head down,
I start to see shapes.
I shout, "MOM!"
Mom says that the dark
can play tricks!

16

It's just car lights shining
on a scarf and a ball.
Still, it's hard to sleep.
"I have a plan,"
Mom tells me.

17

The Flying Machine

by Jeri Cipriano

Table of Contents

Comprehension Check

Retell

Tell a partner why the Wright brothers are famous. Use the pictures to help you.

Think and Compare

1. What happened after the Wright brothers' 12-second flight?

2. Where would you like to take a plane ride to?

3. Why do you think it is good for people to be able to travel by air?

16

Who Were the Wright Brothers?

Orville and Wilbur Wright were inventors. Their dream was to build a flying machine.

As children, they liked to find out how things worked. As grownups, they worked in a bike shop.

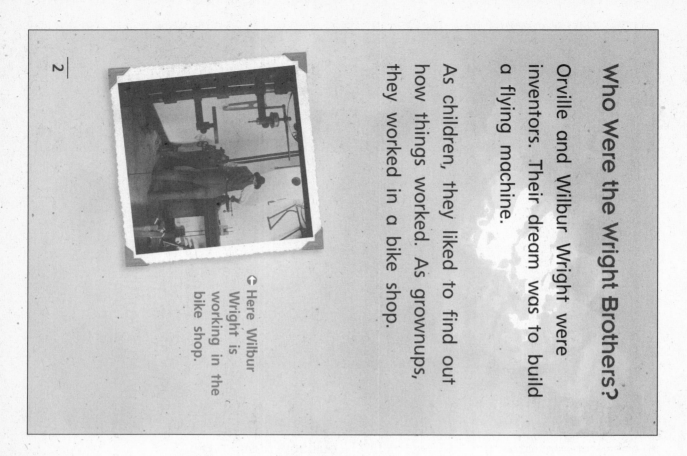

⌒ Here Wilbur Wright is working in the bike shop.

The Flying Machine

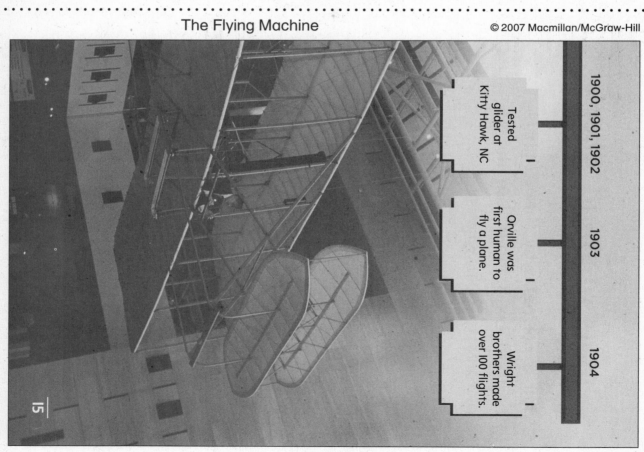

1900, 1901, 1902	1903	1904
Tested glider at Kitty Hawk, NC	Orville was first human to fly a plane.	Wright brothers made over 100 flights.

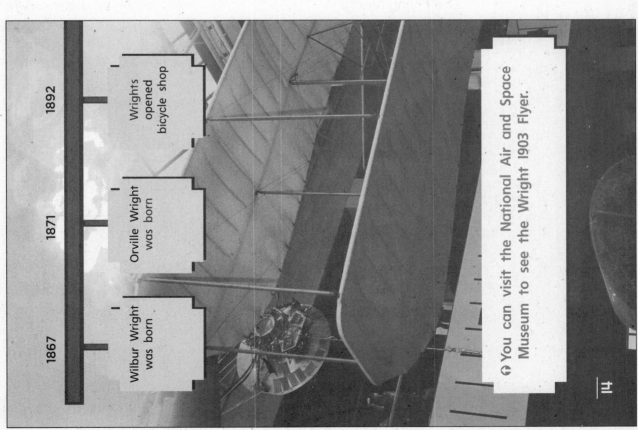

Orville and Wilbur Wright rented, sold, and made bicycles.

3

1867 Wilbur Wright was born

1871 Orville Wright was born

1892 Wrights opened bicycle shop

You can visit the National Air and Space Museum to see the Wright 1903 Flyer.

4

In 1900, the Wright brothers built a glider with two wings. Each wing was covered with cloth. They flew their glider like a kite.

⬑ The two brothers held the ropes tightly.

4

The Flying Machine

The Wright brothers bravely followed their dream to fly. Today people fly to places all over the world. Thanks to the Wright brothers, people can fly!

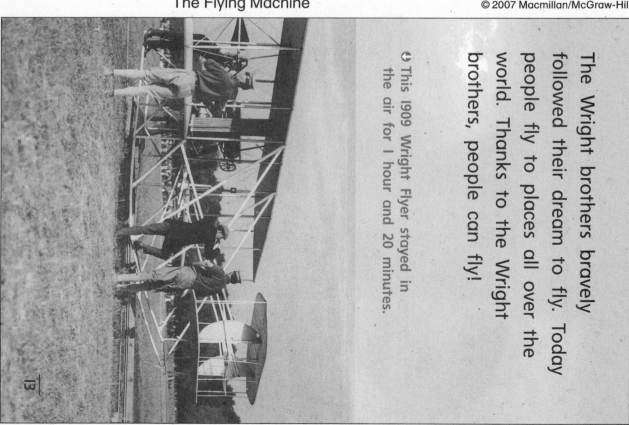

⬐ This 1909 Wright Flyer stayed in the air for 1 hour and 20 minutes.

13

After testing the glider, one brother got on the glider. Then he would glide in the air.

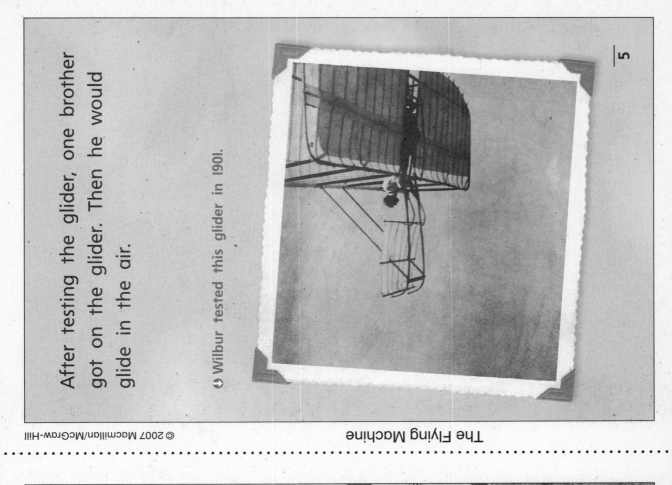

↳ Wilbur tested this glider in 1901.

5

The Wright brothers made many more planes. Each new plane was better than the ones before. The new airplanes could go far. They could stay up longer.

↳ This is a drawing for an early airplane.

12

The Wright brothers made and tested many gliders. With each new discovery they made a better glider.

☝ In 1902, Wilbur steered his glider to the right.

6

The Flying Machine

© 2007 Macmillan/McGraw-Hill

The flight lasted just 12 seconds. But it showed that their flying machine worked. Those 12 seconds would change how people traveled.

☝ Orville used his hands and feet to move the wings and to steer.

11

The Wright brothers looked at birds to see how they fly. The brothers saw birds fly up or down. They saw that birds could turn or circle. The Wright brothers wanted their glider to do those things, too.

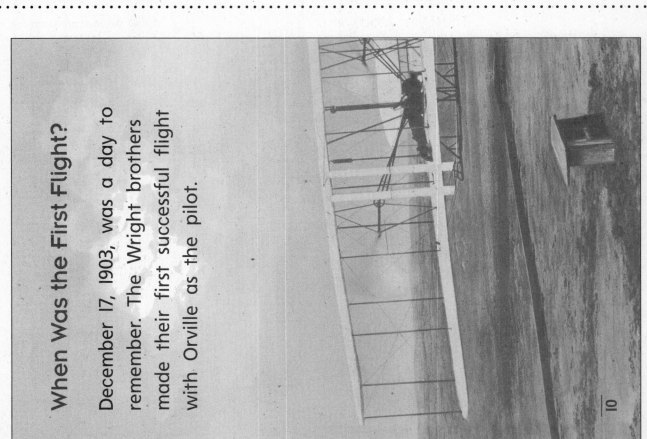

The Wright brothers ↑ watched birds use their wings and tail to fly.

7

When Was the First Flight?

December 17, 1903, was a day to remember. The Wright brothers made their first successful flight with Orville as the pilot.

10

The Wright brothers worked on a new kind of airplane. They added propellers to their plane. A propeller goes round and round.

The Flying Machine

The brothers added an engine. They made it light, so the plane could be lifted into the air.

⟳ On December 14, 1903, Wilbur tried to fly, but the machine did not work.

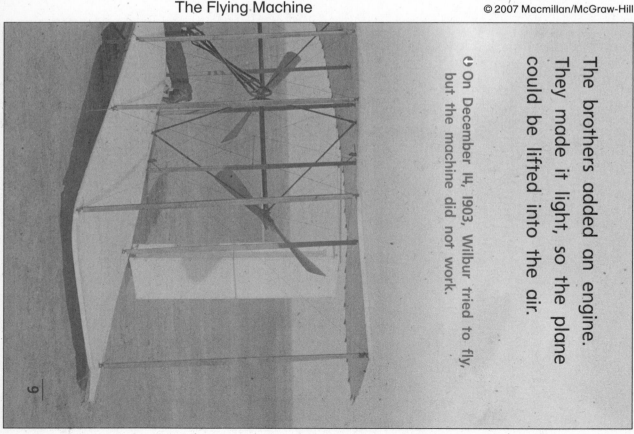

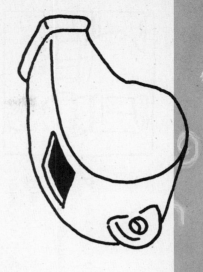

Dear Family Member:

I'm reading *Whistle for Willie* in class this week. It's about a boy who wishes he could whistle. He tries hard. He must feel sad. The author doesn't say he's sad. I just know how I feel when I can't do something. When I understand things the author doesn't say, I'm making inferences.

This Week's Skills

Comprehension: make inferences

Phonics: the sound of *or* in *fork*

Spelling: words with *or*

(fold here)

Name _____

Word Workout

WORDS TO KNOW

early   nothing   along   thought

errand   instead   suddenly

My ABCs Let's read the words in A-B-C order. Then we can use each word in a sentence.

MY SPELLING WORDS

born   cork   corn

fork   horn   pork

Art Time Draw pictures for the two spelling words that rhyme with **pork**. Then label each picture. Next, draw pictures for the two spelling words that rhyme with **born** and label them.

What Next?

Look at each picture and read the sentence. Then circle the letter of the sentence that best tells what will happen next.

Jill put clothes in her suitcase.
Then . . .

a. she took the clothes out again.

b. she went to visit Grandma.

Jake saw the present on the table.
Then . . .

a. he opened it.

b. he went out to play.

Anna opened the refrigerator.
Then . . .

a. she took out the milk.

b. she went to school.

Ray felt cold. So . . .

a. he put on his bathing suit.

b. he put on a sweater.

Beth saw that it was raining. So . . .

a. she went to the beach.

b. she stayed home and read.

Queridos familiares:

Estoy leyendo *Whistle for Willie* en la clase esta semana. Es acerca de un niño que le gustaría poder silbar. Él lo intenta con mucho afán. Se debe sentir triste. El autor no dice que él está triste pero sé cómo yo me siento cuando no puedo hacer algo. Cuando comprendo cosas que el autor no dice, estoy haciendo inferencias.

Destrezas de la semana

Comprensión: hacer inferencias

Fonética: el sonido de **or** como en fork

Ortografía: palabras con **or**

(Fold here)

Nombre _____

Ejercicio de palabras

PALABRAS DE VOCABULARIO

early	nothing	along	thought
errand	instead	suddenly

Mi abecedario Leamos las palabras en orden alfabético. Luego usemos cada palabra en una oración.

PALABRAS DE ORTOGRAFÍA

born	cork	corn
fork	horn	pork

Vamos a dibujar Haz dibujos para las dos palabras de ortografía que riman con la palabra **pork**. Después rotula cada dibujo. Luego, haz dibujos para las dos palabras de ortografía que riman con la palabra **born** y rotúlalos.

Tres en raya

Observa las ilustraciones. Escoge una. Di lo que la persona está haciendo y qué piensas que va a ocurrir. Luego usa un creyón de color rojo para escribir una X sobre el cuadrado. Ahora me toca a mí. El que tenga tres X en raya, ya sea en sentido horizontal o vertical, gana el juego.

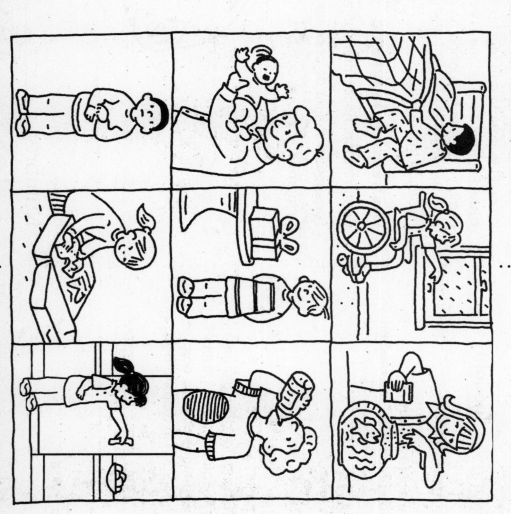

No More Mort the Short!

No More Mort the Short!

by Kenneth Corin

illustrated by Mircea Catusanu

The prize was a big, round pin.
Cory said, "Now I'll have to
name you Mort the Math Whiz!"

26

Mort is smaller than most of the children in his class. So Mort's pal Cory named him Mort the Short.

© 2007 Macmillan/McGraw-Hill

That made Mort study more than before! The Math Bee came. Cory did well, but Mort got the Grand Prize!

No More Mort the Short!

Mort isn't good at running
or other sports.
But he tries hard.
He runs until he is worn out.
His mom yells, "Stop, Mort!"

But Cory gave Mort a hard time.
"You won't win," she said.
"I'm better at math than
you are."

At school, Miss Loren said,
"We will have a Math Bee."
Mort felt happy. He knew
that he could win.

22

© 2007 Macmillan/McGraw-Hill

Mort did his math from
morning until night.
He added up the numbers
that his mom named.
He got each sum right!

23

Jill's Shoelaces

by Janine Scott

illustrated by Louise Alexandra Ellis

Table of Contents

Comprehension Check

Retell the Story

Use an Inference Chart to help you make an inference about the story.

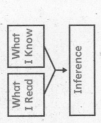

Think and Compare

1. Why do you think Jill wanted to learn to tie her shoelaces?

2. Did you ever try to do something new? How did you learn to do it?

3. What things do all children have to learn to do as they get older?

Jill Gets Help

Early one day, Jill tried to tie her shoelaces. But she could not tie them.

"You will be able to do it one day soon," said Jill's mother. "Put on your shoes with the straps instead." Then she left to do an errand.

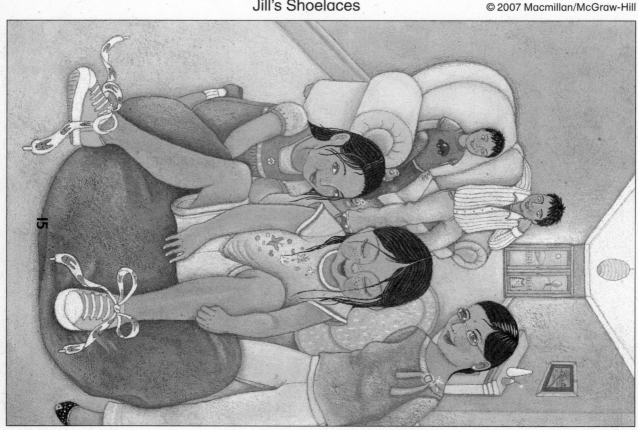

2

15

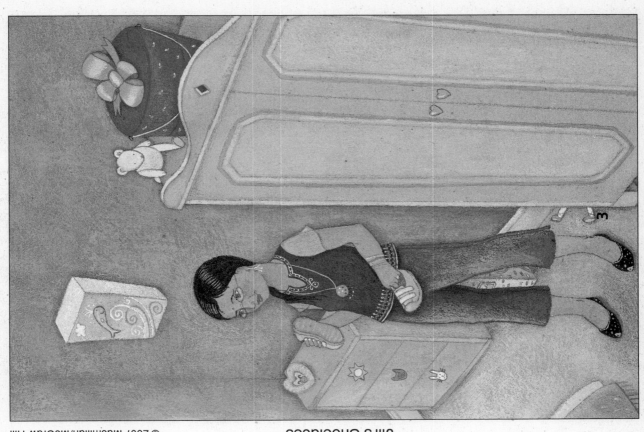

3

The next day, Jill's family gave Jill new shoelaces. They had pictures of bunny rabbits on them. Jill loved them. She tied them over and over and over again.

14

Jill's Shoelaces

At last, Jill had done it! She had tied her shoes. She was so happy. She ran to show her mother. "That's great," said her mother.

13

12

Along came Jill's sister, Molly. "Pretend the laces are snakes. Tie the snakes together, like this," said Molly.

Jill kept getting her snakes tied in knots.

"Put on your sandals," said Molly. "They do not have laces."

5

Jill sat down and tried again.
Along came Jill's brother, Josh.
He sat down with her.

9

Jill's Shoelaces

Jill made the shoelaces into
two big bunny ears. Then she
put one bunny ear around,
under, and through the other
bunny ear.

"Pretend the laces are long worms. Tie the worms together, like this," said Josh.

But Jill kept getting her worms tied in knots.

7

Early that night, Jill went out to the yard. She thought she would never learn how to tie her laces.

Then Jill saw her rabbit. His ears looked like two long shoelaces. Suddenly she thought she would try it her way.

10

More Help for Jill

Jill's mother and father showed her, too. Her mother said nothing about snakes.

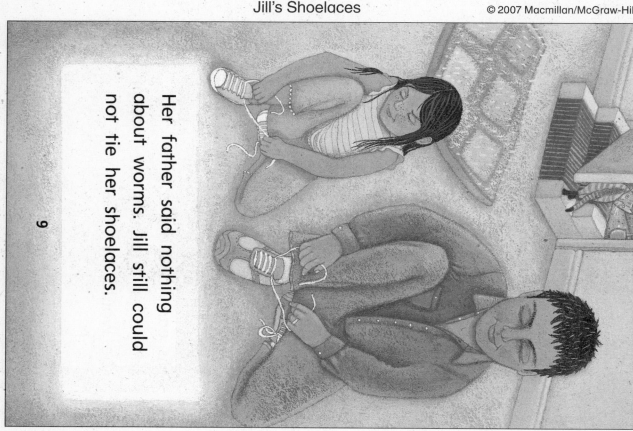

8

Her father said nothing about worms. Jill still could not tie her shoelaces.

9

Home-School Connection

Dear Family Member:

I'm reading A Fruit Is a Suitcase for Seeds in class this week. I'm learning that some fruits or vegetables have many small seeds. Some have big seeds. Some have only one seed! I'm learning how to put things into groups. When I'm done reading, I bet I'll have many groups.

This Week's Skills

Comprehension: classify and categorize

Phonics: vowel sounds er, ur, and ir

Spelling: words with ir, ur, and er

Name _____

·····(fold here)·····

Word Workout

WORDS TO KNOW

places	animals	from	ground
beautiful	crowded	part	tiny

Art Time We can draw a picture of *animals* living in *beautiful places*. Then you can tell me a story about where the *animals are from* using the words.

SPELLING WORDS

bird	burn	dirt
fern	fur	her

Write It Right I'll read each word with you. Tell me if the word has the vowel sound you hear in *turn*. Can you name the letters that stand for that sound? Then dip your finger in water and write the word on the counter as you spell it.

Soccer Teams

We'll each make a scorecard with "Food" on one side and "Clothing" on the other. Then we'll each choose a page or a goal. Flip a coin. If you flip "Heads," write the first word on your page on the correct side of your scorecard. Move a marker one space from the center toward your goal. If you flip "Tails," write the word and move your marker two spaces. I'll go next. Whoever reaches his or her goal first, wins.

coat   skirt   meat   socks   peas

shorts   eggs   cap   belt   bread

shirt   beans   hat   skirt   oatmeal

pizza   scarf   pants   popcorn   roast beef

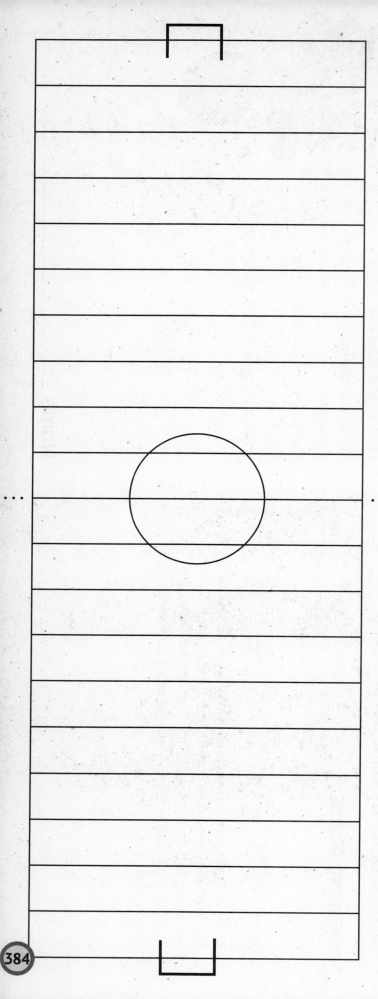

Queridos familiares:

Estoy leyendo *A Fruit Is a Suitcase for Seeds* en la clase esta semana. Estoy aprendiendo que algunas frutas o verduras tienen muchas semillas pequeñas. Otras tienen semillas grandes. ¡Y otras tienen sólo una semilla! Estoy aprendiendo a cómo poner las cosas en grupos. Cuando termine de leer, apuesto a que tendré muchos grupos.

Destrezas de la semana

Comprensión: clasificar y categorizar

Fonética: sonidos de vocales er, ur y ir

Ortografía: palabras con ir, ur y er

·····(Fold here)·····

© Macmillan/McGraw-Hill

Nombre _____

Ejercicio de palabras

PALABRAS DE VOCABULARIO

places	animals	from	ground
beautiful	crowded	part	tiny

Vamos a dibujar Podemos dibujar un dibujo de *animals* que viven en lugares que son *beautiful*. Luego dime un cuento sobre donde los *animals* son *from* y usas las palabras.

PALABRAS DE ORTOGRAFÍA

bird	burn	dirt
fern	fur	her

Escribir correctamente Voy a leer cada palabra contigo. Dime si la palabra tiene el sonido de la vocal en la palabra *turn*. ¿Cuáles son las letras que significa ese sonido? Luego, mójate el dedo en un vaso con agua y escribe la palabra sobre la mesa mientras la deletreas.

Equipos de fútbol

Cada uno de nosotros va a hacer una tarjeta con la palabra *Food* de un lado y la palabra *Clothing* del otro lado. Tira una moneda. Si sale *heads*, escribe la primera palabra de tu lista en el lado correcto de tu tarjeta. Mueve tu ficha un espacio desde el lado correcto de tu tarjeta. Si sale *tails*, escribe la palabra y mueve tu ficha dos espacios. Luego me toca a mí. El primero que llega a la portería gana el juego.

coat	skirt	meat	socks	peas
shorts	eggs	cap	belt	bread

pizza	shirt	beans	hat	skirt	oatmeal
	scarf	pants	popcorn	roast beef

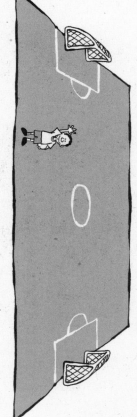

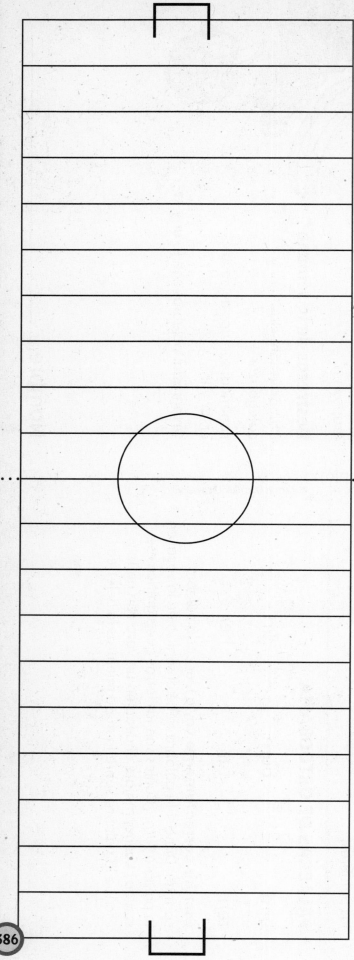

This page is intentionally blank.

Miss Mirth's Herb Garden

Miss Mirth's
Herb Garden
dill
mint
chives
by Maria Arroyo
illustrated by Nan Brooks

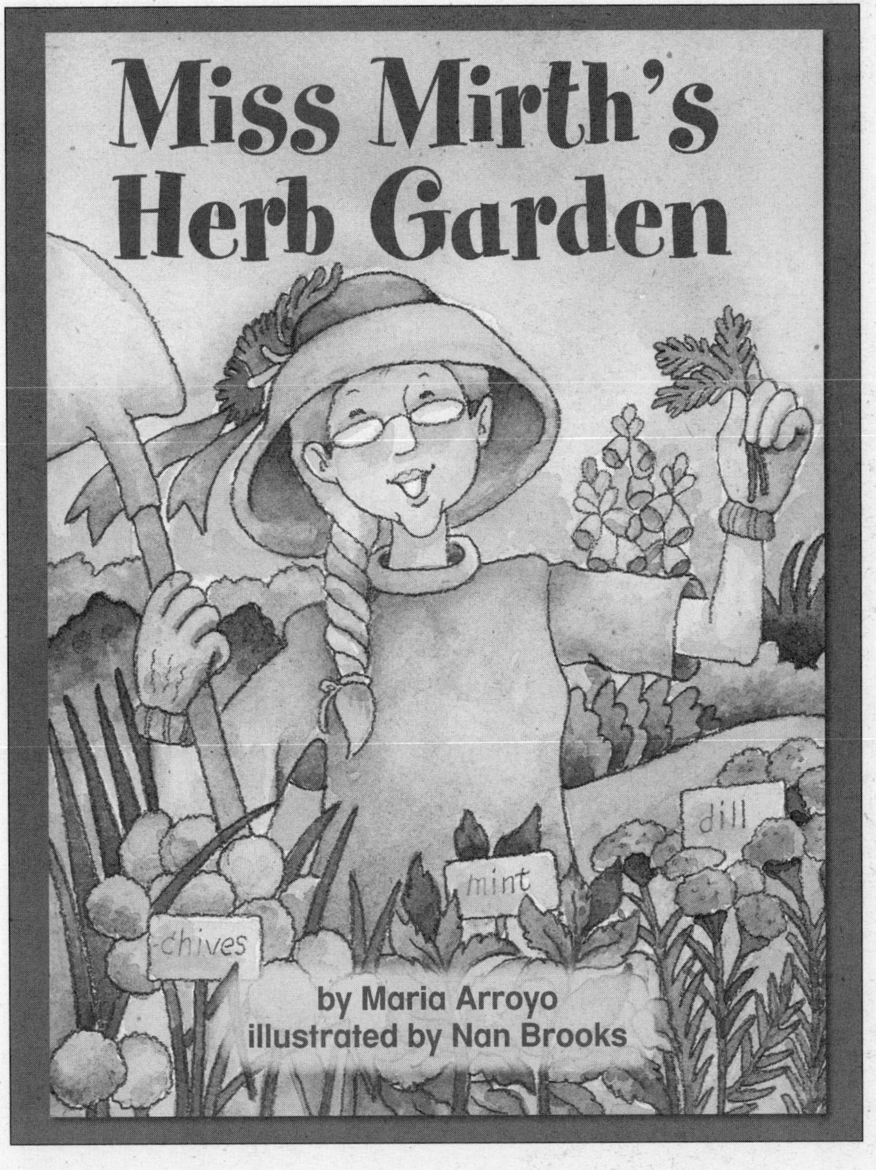

Miss Mirth has a garden
filled with herbs and flowers.
The thought of it makes
Miss Mirth smile.
Her friends love the garden, too.

28

This page is intentionally blank.

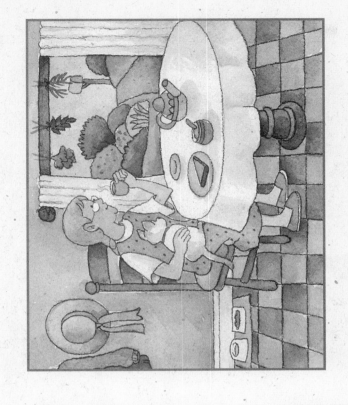

Miss Mirth's Herb Garden

Miss Mirth is up early today.

This is her birthday!

"It's my seventy-third!" says Miss Mirth.

"Who will come along?"

Then lots of people come!
"Happy birthday!" they yell.
"We did not forget you!"

"You didn't!" Miss Mirth beams. "I'm so glad!"

Miss Mirth checks her mail.
There is nothing in her box.
A bird chirps.
Nothing else makes a peep.

30

Miss Mirth picks an herb.
It's green and curly.
She puts it in an urn.
She feels a teeny bit sad.

31

Growing Strawberries

by Sarah Tatler

Table of Contents

Growing Strawberries

Comprehension Check

Retell

Use a Classify and Categorize Chart to sort fruits by color.

Red Fruits	Yellow Fruits
1	1
2	2
3	3

Think and Compare

1. Look back at page 11. How can you keep birds and other little animals away from your strawberry plants?

2. Have you ever eaten strawberries? Do you like them? Why or why not?

3. Does growing strawberries look easy? Explain your answer.

16

What Is a Strawberry?

A strawberry is a fruit. Some strawberries are big and some are little.

Most strawberries are bright red.

Of course, the best way to eat a strawberry is to pop one in your mouth.

Growing Strawberries

© 2007 Macmillan/McGraw-Hill

15

There are over 200 seeds on a strawberry.

Take a closer look at a strawberry.

It has seeds on the outside. Can you see the tiny seeds?

3

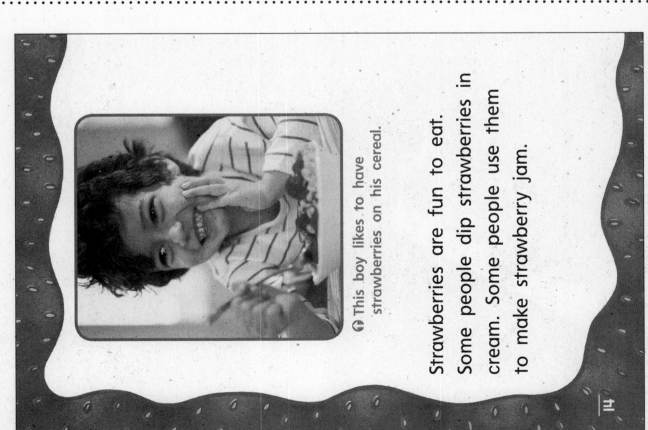

This boy likes to have strawberries on his cereal.

Strawberries are fun to eat. Some people dip strawberries in cream. Some people use them to make strawberry jam.

4

Strawberries grow on strawberry plants on the ground. They get their beautiful red color as they grow ripe.

6 People pick strawberries when they are ripe.

This is a strawberry farm.

13

People can buy strawberries at a market like this.

Here are some boxes of bright red strawberries. They are sweet and juicy! Lots of people buy strawberries to eat.

5

Who Likes Strawberries?

Many people like strawberries. People can grow strawberries in most parts of the United States.

The United States of America

The states where farmers grow the most strawberries are colored in red.

12

How Do Strawberries Grow?

Strawberry plants need lots of sun. Long stems called runners grow close to the ground. A new strawberry plant grows from each runner.

Look at the parts of a strawberry plant. Find the beautiful flower. Then find the fruit.

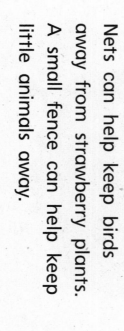

9

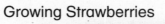

⊕ This turtle looks for strawberries to eat.

Nets can help keep birds away from strawberry plants. A small fence can help keep little animals away.

11

flower

leaf

fruit

runner

roots

7

Animals like strawberries. As your plants grow, you will need to watch for animals. Birds, turtles, and bugs eat strawberry plants. It's easy for an animal to eat the fruit and nibble on the leaves.

10

Strawberries are easy plants to grow.

1. First find a place that gets at least six hours of sun.

2. Next dig holes for the little plants. Put the holes 12 inches apart. They should not be crowded together.

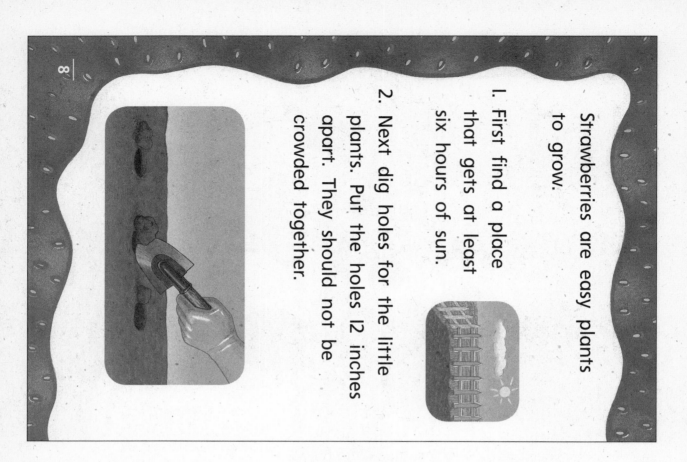

Growing Strawberries

3. Put the plants in the holes. Press the soil around each plant. Make sure the soil covers the tops of the roots.

4. Next water the plants.

5. Pick the strawberries when they are ripe.

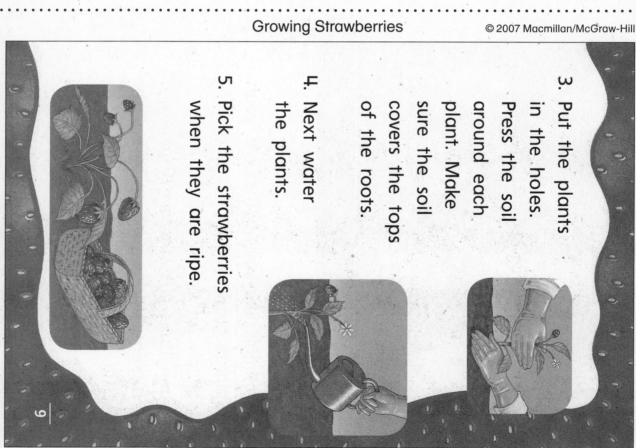

Home-School Connection

Dear Family Member:

I'm reading *Dot and Jabber and the Big Bug Mystery* in class this week. I learned how to use pictures in a story to help me better understand it. The pictures may give me information that the author doesn't tell me. For example, Dot and Jabber are looking for bugs, but the bugs are hiding! I am using the pictures to help me find them as I read.

This Week's Skills

Comprehension: use illustrations

Phonics: sounds of ou and ow as in *bounce* and *plow*

Spelling: words with ow and ou

(fold here)

Name _____

Word Workout

WORDS TO KNOW

other   gone   been

clues   invisible   searching

Sentence Time I'll make up a sentence for each word. I'll say "blank" where the word belongs in the sentence. See if you can fill in the blank.

SPELLING WORDS

cow   how   mouse

mouth   out   town

Sort the Words Let's fold a piece of lined paper in half. Write *ow* and *ou* at the top of each half. Write your spelling words in the right list. Then try to add at least one more word with the same vowel letters to each list.

Where Are the Letters?

We're going to play Follow the Directions. All you'll need is crayons. We'll read each direction and do what it tells us to do.

1. Color the mouse gray.

2. Give the goose a yellow bill.

3. Color the bird blue.

4. Color the bench orange.

5. Make the grass green.

6. Some capital letters are hiding! Find two. Color them red.

Let's make up a story about the picture.

Queridos familiares:

Estoy leyendo *Dot and Jabber and the Big Bug* *Mystery* en la clase esta semana. Aprendí cómo usar las ilustraciones en un cuento para entenderlo mejor. Las ilustraciones me pueden dar información que el autor no me dice. Por ejemplo, Dot y Jabber están buscando insectos, ¡pero los insectos se ocultan! Uso las ilustraciones como ayuda para encontrar los insectos mientras leo.

Destrezas de la semana

Comprensión: usar las ilustraciones

Fonética: los sonidos de *ou* y *ow* como en *bounce* y *plow*

Ortografía: palabras con **ow** y **ou**

(fold here)

Nombre _____

Ejercicio de palabras

PALABRAS DE VOCABULARIO

other	been
gone	
clues	searching
invisible	

Tiempo de oraciones Voy a inventar una oración para cada palabra. Di *blank* en el lugar donde va la palabra en la oración. Fíjate si puedes completar la oración.

PALABRAS DE ORTOGRAFÍA

cow	how
	mouse
mouth	out
	town

Clasificar las palabras Vamos a doblar un papel con renglones a la mitad. Escribe **ow** y **ou** en la parte de arriba de cada mitad. Escribe tus palabras de ortografía en la lista correcta. Luego, agrega por lo menos una palabra más con las mismas vocales a cada lista.

¿Dónde están las letras?

Vamos a jugar un juego. Sigue las instrucciones. Todo lo que necesitarás son unos creyones. Vamos a leer cada instrucción y hacer lo que nos dice que hagamos.

1. Color the mouse gray.

2. Give the goose a yellow bill.

3. Color the bird blue.

4. Color the bench orange.

5. Make the grass green.

6. Some capital letters are hiding! Find two. Color them red.

Let's make up a story about the picture.

A Proud Brown Ant

retold by Lily Wallace

illustrated by Barry Rockwell

Crouching down, she slowly lifted up the cake. Step by step, the ant made it home! The cake would last all winter. The ant had never felt so proud.

8

A little brown ant had a very big family. The ants seemed the same, but the little brown ant was just a bit smaller than the rest.

2

The ant asked the animals she met for help. Each one told her, "No. I will not help."

"Well," pouted the ant, "then I'll have to do it myself!"

7

When it gets cold in most
places, ants gather food
for the winter. So all the
ants set out fast! The little
brown ant was left alone.

A Proud Brown Ant

3

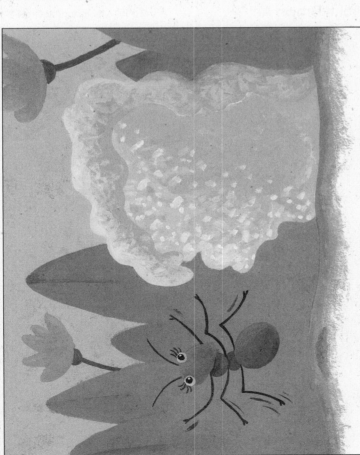

The ant got closer. "Cake!"
she cried loudly. "It's a big,
beautiful hunk of sweet cake.
How will I get it home from
here? I am much too small."

6

"Wait for me," she shouted.
But no one heard her.

When the little brown ant met
up with the rest, they were
on their way back home.

4

The little brown ant frowned.
"All the food is gone now.
How will I eat?"

The ant sat down to rest. She
saw something on the ground.

5

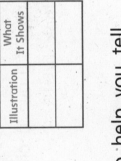

The Painted Lady Butterfly

by Nancy J. Nielsen
illustrated by Lyuba Bogan

Table of Contents

Comprehension Check

Retell the Story

Look back at the pictures in this book. Use an Illustration Chart to help you tell what the pictures show.

Illustration	What It Shows

Think and Compare

1. What can you learn from the picture on page 8 that you cannot learn from the words?

2. Sara saw her favorite butterfly. How did she feel when she saw it? What is your favorite animal to see?

3. What did you learn about butterflies that you never knew?

16

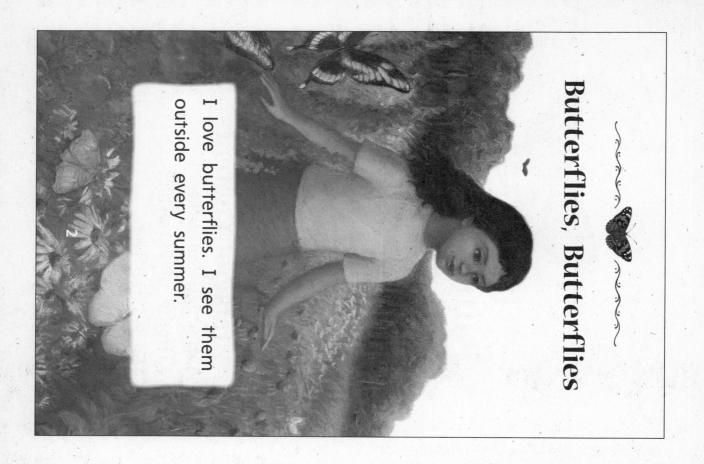

Butterflies, Butterflies, Butterflies

I love butterflies. I see them outside every summer.

2

The Painted Lady Butterfly © 2007 Macmillan/McGraw-Hill

"I'm going to come back to see the Painted Lady," I said. "And now I have a clue about where to look first!"

15

Butterflies have names. This butterfly is the Painted Lady. I like other butterflies, but I like that one best.

3

"Now, I see why you couldn't find the Painted Lady. It was on your shirt all the time!" the helper said.

She gently lifted it off and showed it to me and the others. It was beautiful.

4

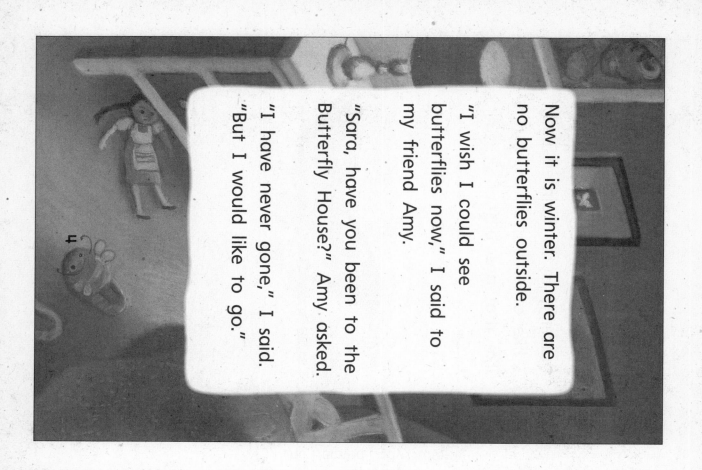

Now it is winter. There are no butterflies outside.

"I wish I could see butterflies now," I said to my friend Amy.

"Sara, have you been to the Butterfly House?" Amy asked.

"I have never gone," I said. "But I would like to go."

4

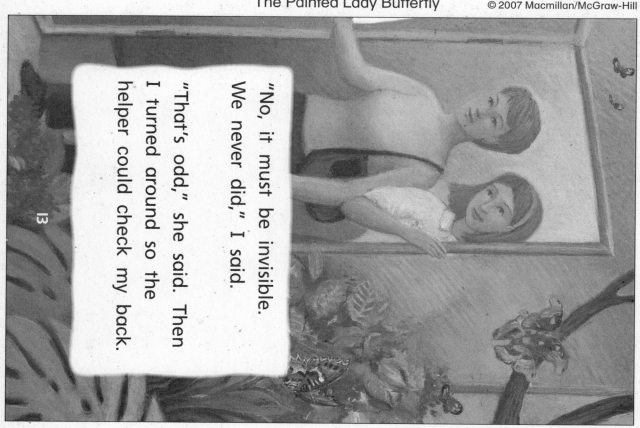

"No, it must be invisible. We never did," I said.

"That's odd," she said. Then I turned around so the helper could check my back.

13

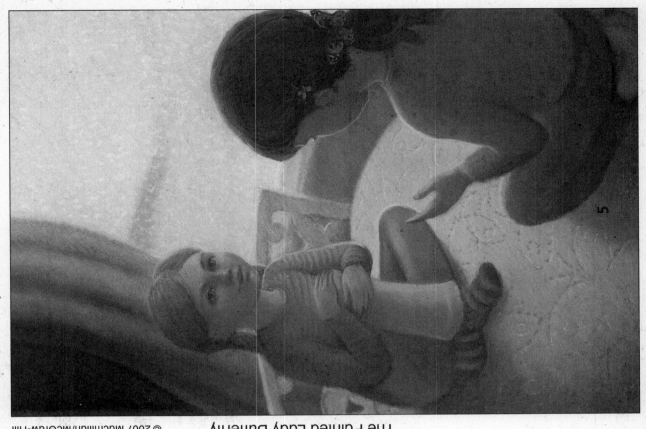

5

The Painted Lady

"We have to go now," Amy's mother said. "The helpers will check to see if you have any butterflies on you."

"Did you find the Painted Lady?" one helper asked.

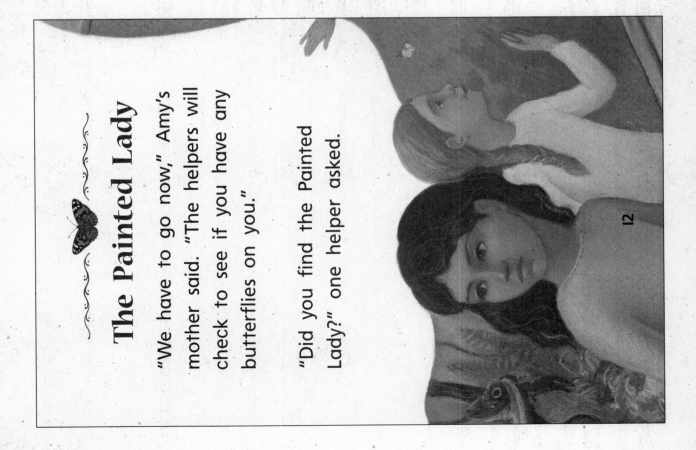

12

A House of Butterflies

A week later Amy called.

"Would you like to come to the Butterfly House, Sara? My mom and I are going."

"Yes!" I said. "Just beep when you get here."

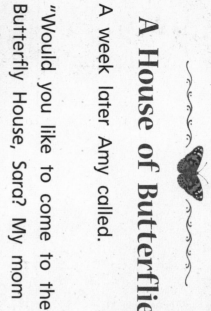

9

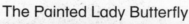

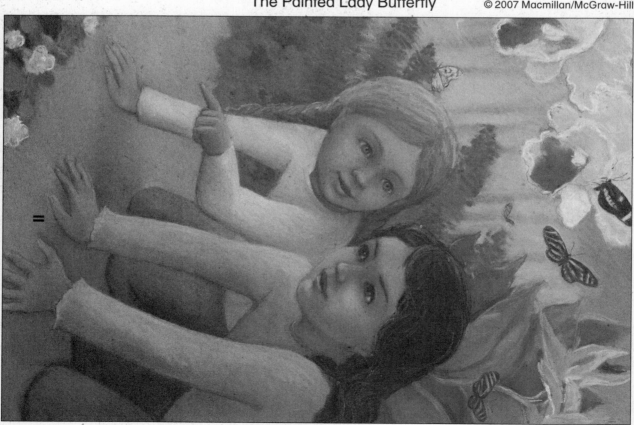

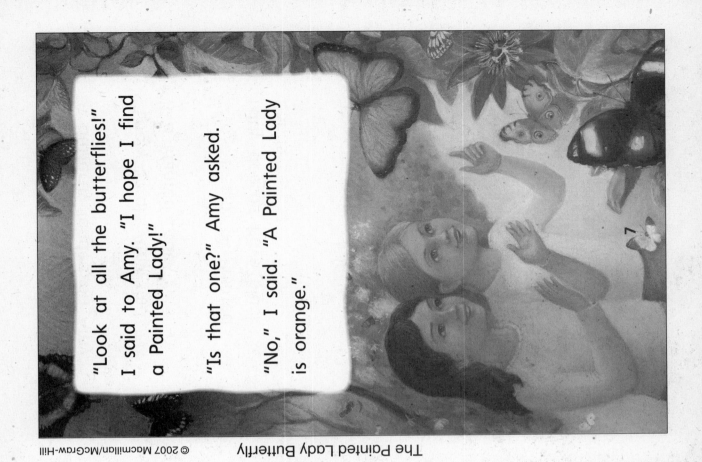

"Look at all the butterflies!" I said to Amy. "I hope I find a Painted Lady!"

"Is that one?" Amy asked.

"No," I said. "A Painted Lady is orange."

7

"There it is!" said Amy.

"No, it's not," I said. "A Painted Lady has black and white spots."

We looked all around. We looked under plants and on plants. We looked everywhere, but it was gone!

10

A butterfly landed on Amy.

"Look, Sara!" Amy said. "Is it a Painted Lady?"

"No," I said. "A Painted Lady doesn't have black bands."

8

© 2007 Macmillan/McGraw-Hill

"I have never been here before," I said to a helper. "Do you have a Painted Lady?"

"Yes," she said. "Search! You will find one."

9

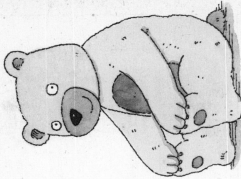

Dear Family Member:

I'm reading *Little Bear Goes to the Moon* in class this week. We reviewed how to make predictions when reading. My own experiences and what is in the story help me to predict what might happen next. Little Bear wants to fly to t moon! I predict that Little Bear not be able to fly like a bird, but need to read on to find out!

This Week's Skills

Comprehension: make predictio

Phonics: the sound of oo as in *look*

Spelling: words with **oo**

...(fold here)...

© Macmillan/McGraw-Hill

Word Workout

WORDS TO KNOW

bear	birds	Earth	table
fooling	guess	helmet	space

Writing Time A sentence begins with a capital letter and ends with a mark such as a **.**, **?**, or **!**. We can write each word in a sentence and put the correct mark at the end.

SPELLING WORDS

book	cook	hood
look	took	wood

Crossword Time Look at the crossword below. We can make puzzles like it. We can connect words using the letters **oo**.

	W		
B	O	O	K
	O		
	D		

Name _____

What Will Happen?

Let's look at the first picture on this page. Can you find the picture on the next page that shows what will happen next? We'll draw a line to connect the two pictures. Then we'll do the same for the other pictures on this page.

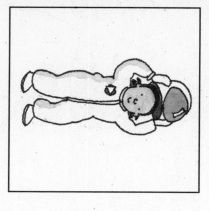

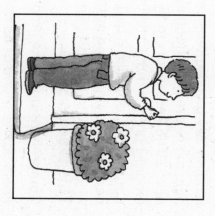

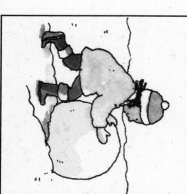

When we are done, we can tell a story about each set of pictures.

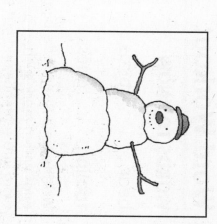

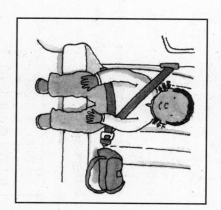

Conexión con el hogar

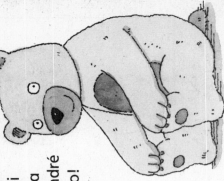

Queridos familiares:

Estoy leyendo *Little Bear Goes to the Moon* en la clase esta semana. Repasamos cómo hacer predicciones cuando leemos. Mis propias experiencias junto con lo que hay en el cuento me ayudan a predecir lo que podría ocurrir después. ¡Little Bear quiere ir volando a la Luna! Mi predicción es que Little Bear no va a poder volar como un ave, ¡pero tendré que seguir leyendo para averiguarlo!

Destrezas de la semana

Comprensión: hacer predicciones

Fonética: el sonido de **oo** como en *look*

Ortografía: palabras con **oo**

Nombre _____

(fold here)

© Macmillan/McGraw-Hill

Ejercicio de palabras

PALABRAS DE VOCABULARIO

bear	birds	Earth	table
fooling	guess	helmet	space

Tiempo de escribir Una oración comienza con una letra mayúscula y termina con un signo de puntuación, como por ejemplo **.**, **?**, o **!**. Vamos a escribir cada palabra en una oración y colocar el signo de puntuación correcto al final.

PALABRAS DE ORTOGRAFÍA

book	cook	hood
look	took	wood

Tiempo de crucigramas Observa el crucigrama. Armemos crucigramas parecidos. Conectemos palabras con las letras **oo**.

W			
B	O	O	K
	O		
	D		

417

¿Qué va a ocurrir?

Vamos a jugar un juego. Vamos a comenzar donde está la palabra *GO*. Hablemos acerca de la primera ilustración. Luego, tracemos una línea hasta la ilustración que creemos que va a ser la próxima cosa que va a ocurrir. Seguiremos jugando hasta llegar a la palabra *END*.

GO

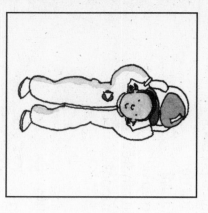

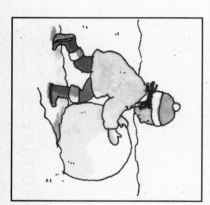

Cuando terminemos, podemos colorear los recuadros en orden, siguiendo cada línea. Luego, podemos contar un cuento acerca de las ilustraciones.

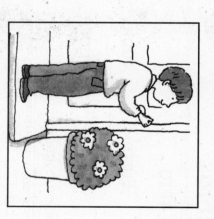

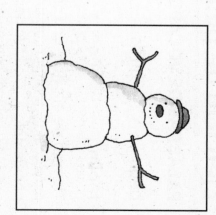

END

We Took a Look at This Camp

by Lucy Floyd

We Took a Look at This Camp

This page is intentionally blank.

Look at him dressed up!
Has he been in space?
No, he is at Space Camp!

10

We Took a Look at This Camp

This page is intentionally blank.

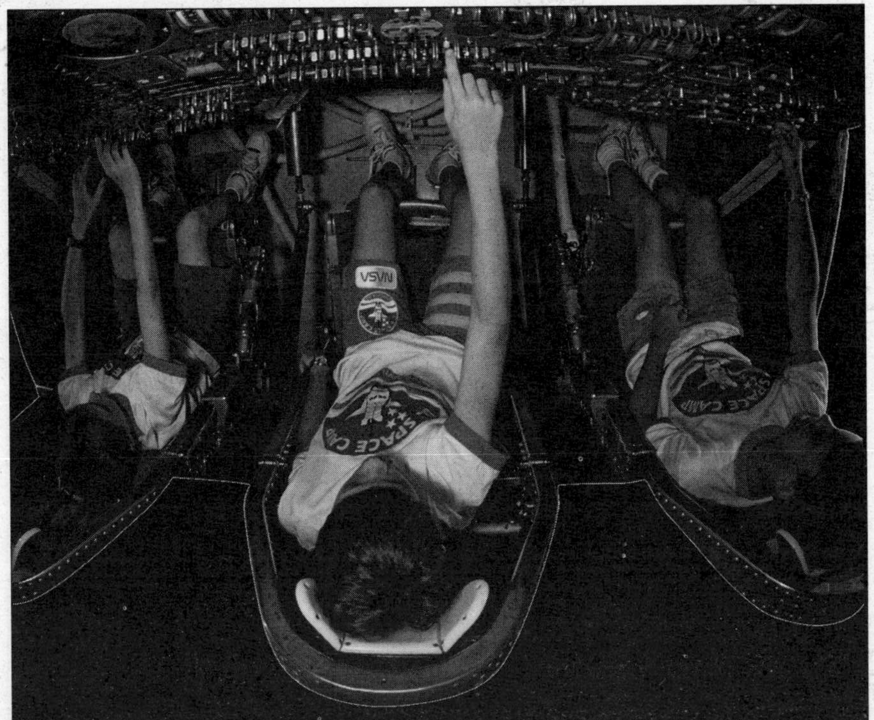

The camp is for kids.

Kids can study and train
like an astronaut.

This girl took a class that
trained her for a space walk!

We Took a Look at This Camp

11

How do astronauts sleep?

Can they cook?

Who took the most trips?

Look in a book, or go to
Space Camp and find out!

14

At this camp kids can see a
real rocket up close.
Then they can make their own!
Kids study other things, too.

12

Kids study the planet Mars.
What do the rocks look like?
Was there a brook on Mars?
Has anyone gone to Mars?
The kids find out at camp.

13

The Trip

by Nancy J. Nielsen

illustrated by Nicole Rutten

Table of Contents

Comprehension Check

Retell the Story

Use a Predictions Chart to check your predictions about the story.

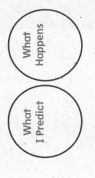

What I Predict

What Happens

Think and Compare

1. Will Bird and Bear want to go to the moon again? Why or why not?

2. Bird and Bear had fun pretending. What do you like to pretend? How does pretending make you feel?

3. Why do you think some people want to go traveling in space?

16

To the Moon

Bird and Bear sat at the lake. It was night, and they were looking at the moon.

"The moon looks flat," said Bird. "But I know it is round like a ball."

"I would love to fly to the moon," said Bear.

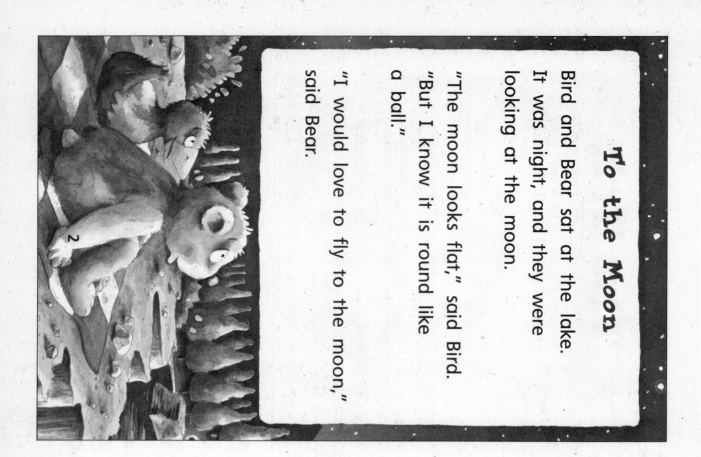

2

"What a good way to fly," said Bird.

"I'm glad you came along," said Bear.

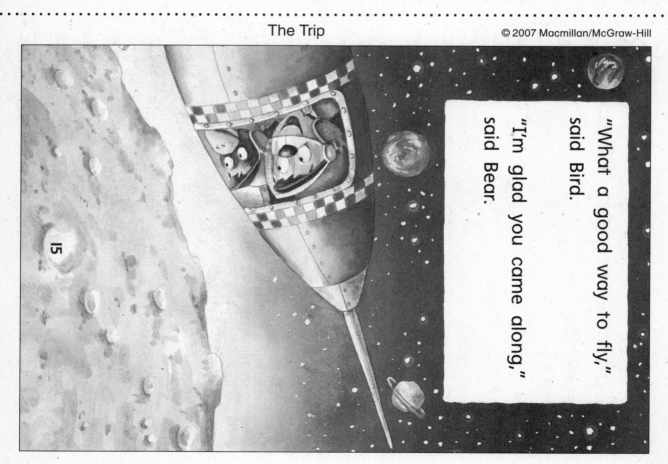

15

The Trip

3

Bear and Bird were on their way to the moon. They looked out the window. They saw that Earth was far, far away.

4

"You're fooling. You can't fly!"
said Bird.

"I could make a spaceship,"
said Bear. "Then I could fly."

4

13

"Ha!" said Bird. "That would take
too long. I could fly to the moon
and be back before you are done."

"You can't fly to the moon,"
said Bear. "It's too far away
in space."

5

Bear lit the rockets.
The spaceship shook.

"Pull that switch," said Bear.
Bird did, and the spaceship
took off.

12

Bye, Bye, Bird

The next day, Bird went to see Bear. Bear had set a table on the grass. There were lots of things on the table.

"Hello, Bear," said Bird. "What are you doing?"

"I'm looking for parts for my spaceship," said Bear. "What are you doing?"

6

"Yes," said Bear. "I'm going to the moon now. I guess you could come, too."

"I would love to," said Bird.

"Put on your helmet," said Bear.

11

"I'm going to the moon," said Bird.

"Have a good trip. Bye, bye, Bird," said Bear.

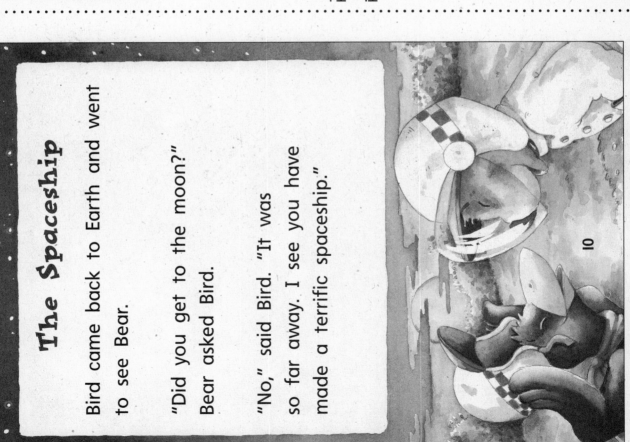

The Spaceship

Bird came back to Earth and went to see Bear.

"Did you get to the moon?" Bear asked Bird.

"No," said Bird. "It was so far away. I see you have made a terrific spaceship."

10

Bird shook his wings and took off.
He went up and up into the sky.
Bear looked up from Earth.
She saw Bird high in the sky.

8

Bird huffed and puffed. Bird tried
to go higher. But, he could not get
to the moon.

9

Dear Family Member:

I'm reading "Cool Jobs" in class this week. I learned how to classify by putting things that are alike into groups. I make groups about things that have something in common. As I read "Cool Jobs," I am thinking about what I might like to do when I grow up. There are so many special jobs! In the article I'm reading, there is a zoo dentist who works on the teeth of wild animals! I wonder what other cool jobs there are.

This Week's Skills

Comprehension: classify and categorize

Phonics: the sound of **oo** as in moon

Spelling: words with **oo**

Name _____

(fold here)

© Macmillan/McGraw-Hill

Word Workout

WORDS TO KNOW

only   laugh   goes   ever

interesting   ordinary

Sentence Time Make up a sentence for each word.

SPELLING WORDS

broom   cool   moon

pool   room   soon

Rhyme Time Tell me which pairs of words rhyme. Spell each pair of rhyming words. Can you think of another word that rhymes with each pair?

Soccer Teams

Put a penny in the center of the field and choose your goalpost. Flip a coin. If it lands on Heads, move your penny to the first word on the top of your list. If it lands on Tails, move it to the second word. Does your word name an animal or a person? Put a checkmark in your scorecard. We'll take turns and see who has more animals and who has more people.

Animals	People

Animals	People

puppy
children
mother
crocodile
llama
grandfather
brother
snake
pelican
boy

father
ape
dolphin
neighbor
turtle
aunt
rabbit
relatives
girl
elephant

Queridos familiares:

Estoy leyendo *Cool Jobs* en la clase esta semana. Aprendí cómo clasificar organizando las cosas que son parecidas en grupos. Puedo armar grupos de cosas que tienen algo en común. Mientras leo *Cool Jobs*, pienso sobre las cosas que me gustaría hacer cuando sea grande. ¡Hay tantos trabajos especiales! En el artículo que estoy leyendo, ¡hay un dentista en el zoológico que trabaja con los dientes de los animales salvajes! Me pregunto qué otros trabajos especiales hay.

Destrezas de la semana

Comprensión: clasificar y categorizar

Fonética: el sonido de oo como en moon

Ortografía: palabras con oo

Nombre _____

·······(Fold here.)·······

© Macmillan/McGraw-Hill

Ejercicio de palabras

PALABRAS DE VOCABULARIO

only   laugh   goes   ever

interesting   ordinary

Tiempo de frase Crea una frase para cada palabra.

PALABRAS DE ORTOGRAFÍA

broom   cool   moon

pool   room   soon

Vamos a rimar Dime qué par de palabras riman y deletrea cada par de palabras que rimen. ¿Puedes pensar en alguna otra palabra que rime con cada par de palabras?

433

Equipos de fútbol

Coloca una moneda de un centavo en el centro del campo de fútbol y escoge tu portería. Tira una moneda. Si sale *heads*, mueve tu moneda de un centavo a la primera palabra de tu lista. Si sale *tails*, muévela a la segunda palabra. ¿Tu palabra nombra a un animal o a una persona? Coloca una marca en tu anotador de puntos. Vamos a tomar turnos y ver quién tiene más animales y quién tiene más personas.

puppy

children

mother

crocodile

llama

grandfather

brother

snake

pelican

boy

father

ape

dolphin

neighbor

turtle

aunt

rabbit

relatives

girl

elephant

Animals	People

Animals	People

434

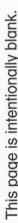

See a Zoo Soon!

by Rosa Acosta

See a Zoo Soon!

This page is intentionally blank.

We can see many animals
at the zoo.
The zoo is a safe home.
Animals get room to roam
and good food to eat.

16

See a Zoo Soon!

This page is intentionally blank.

Zoo keepers care for animals
that live in the zoo.

These elephants get a checkup.
Zoo keepers feed them, too.
The elephants like eating hay!

See a Zoo Soon!

Parrots are beautiful birds.
Look at this bright parrot.
It has room to perch and fly!

Visiting a zoo can be fun.
Let's plan a zoo trip soon!

20

This bear likes to stay cool.
It cools off in the zoo pool.
The bear can swim and run fast.
It's a good thing that it can't
get loose!

18

Many kinds of monkeys
live on the earth.
These monkeys are baboons.
Their zoo home is so rocky!
It has a rock table and bed.

19

The Pilots

by Mario Fuentes

Table of Contents

Comprehension Check

Retell

Look back at the pictures in this book. Use them to help you retell to a classmate what you learned about pilots.

Think and Compare

1. How is flying a helicopter different from flying a large jet plane?

2. Tell why you think a pilot has an exciting job.

3. What other things do pilots fly that were not talked about in this book?

16

Chapter 1
What Is a Pilot?

A pilot is a person who flies a plane. Most people think a pilot has a very interesting job.

◉ This pilot sits in the cockpit of the plane.

The Pilots

Glossary

engine (*EN-jin*) a machine that uses energy to run other machines (*page 8*)

sightseeing (*SIGHT-see-ing*) to go to places of interest (*page 9*)

simulator (*SIM-yuh-lay-tuhr*) something that seems like the real thing (*page 6*)

uniform (*YEW-nuh-fawrm*) special clothes (*page 3*)

Index

This girl wants to know how long the flight will take.

Have you ever been to a busy airport? If you have, you may have seen a pilot dressed in **uniform**. Have you ever asked a pilot a question?

3

Pretend you are on this jet. You hear the pilot.

"We are cleared for takeoff," says the pilot. "Please fasten your seat belts."

Sit back in your seat. Laugh with a friend. Have a wonderful ride!

4

Chapter 2
How Does Someone Get to Be a Pilot?

Someone who learns to fly is a student pilot. A student pilot goes to flight school.

What Do You Learn at Flight School?

- Learn all about airplanes.
- Fly with an instructor.
- Learn to take off.
- Learn how to stay up in the air.
- Learn to land.
- Learn to watch for weather.

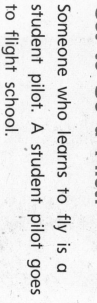

The Pilots

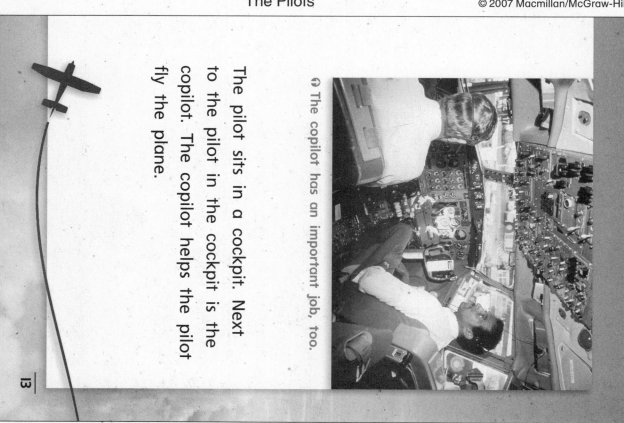

The copilot has an important job, too.

The pilot sits in a cockpit. Next to the pilot in the cockpit is the copilot. The copilot helps the pilot fly the plane.

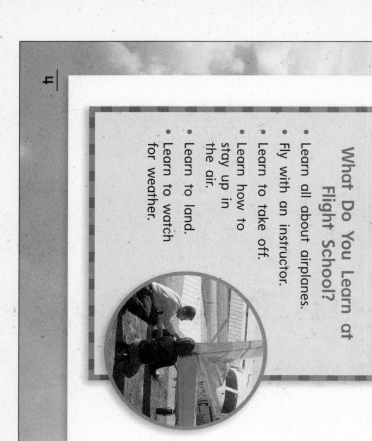

A student pilot flies with an instructor.

Student pilots have to pass two kinds of tests. They have to answer questions on paper. They also have to fly a plane. The students have to show that they can take off, fly, and land the plane.

Some pilots fly huge jets. They take hundreds of people from one place to another.

The pilot will make sure the flight is as safe as can be.

Even pilots who pass their tests spend time training. They can learn to fly different kinds of planes in a flight **simulator**.

6

There are places where only helicopters can fly. They are places where ordinary planes cannot go.

11

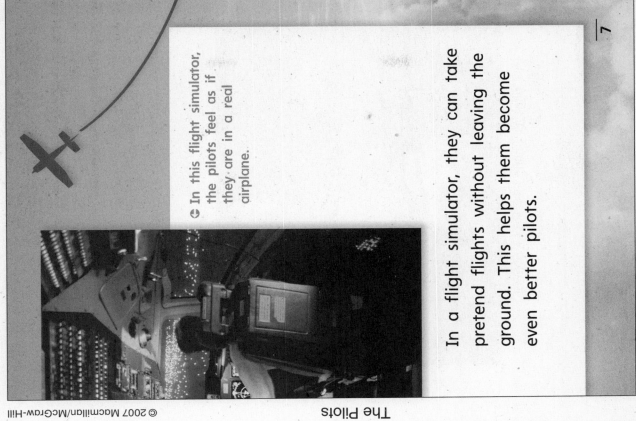

In this flight simulator, the pilots feel as if they are in a real airplane.

In a flight simulator, they can take pretend flights without leaving the ground. This helps them become even better pilots.

Some pilots fly helicopters. A helicopter is different from an ordinary plane. Helicopter pilots can fly forward and fly backward. They also can turn the helicopter in a circle and stay still in the air.

Helicopter pilots can land on snowy mountaintops.

Chapter 3
What Do Pilots Fly?

Most new pilots fly small planes that have one **engine**.

➔ This pilot is giving his plane a final check.

The Pilots

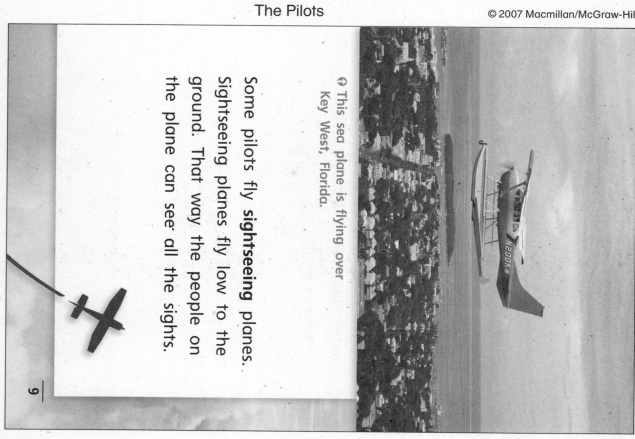

➔ This sea plane is flying over Key West, Florida.

Some pilots fly **sightseeing** planes. Sightseeing planes fly low to the ground. That way the people on the plane can see all the sights.

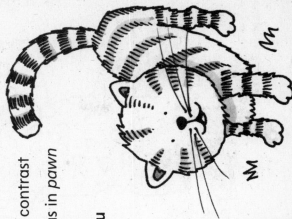

Home-School Connection

Dear Family Member:

I'm reading *A Tiger Cub Grows Up* this week. We are reviewing how to compare and contrast. I compare how things are alike. I contrast how things are different. In this story, I am reading how a tiger cub and a grown-up tiger are alike and different. Little Tara, the tiger cub, is nervous when taking her first bath. Grown-up tigers love to jump into the water and swim.

This Week's Skills

Comprehension: compare and contrast

Phonics: sound of *aw* and *au* as in *pawn* and *pause*

Spelling: words with *aw* and *au*

............(fold here)............

© Macmillan/McGraw-Hill

Name _____

Word Workout

WORDS TO KNOW

across	air	enough	eyes	learn
cub	wild			

Art Time Let's draw a picture of a zoo doctor's office, or think of what a zoo doctor's office looks like. Then we can use the words in sentences to describe your picture.

SPELLING WORDS

cause	claw	dawn
haul	paw	saw

Write It Right With your arm, write each spelling word I say in the air. Then spell it aloud. We can write each word on a piece of paper.

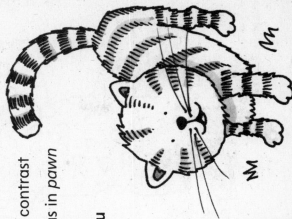

Look What Paul Saw!

Paul went to the circus! Look at the clowns he saw. Let's talk about how the clowns are alike and different as we answer the questions on the next page.

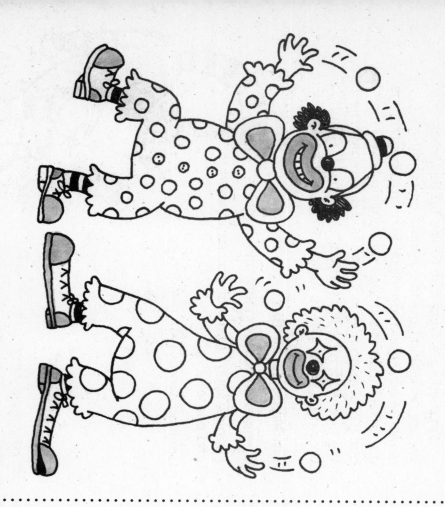

How are the clowns alike?

- What are they both doing?
- What is around their necks?
- What shape is on their suits?
- How else are the alike?

How are the clowns different?

- What shapes are their eyes?
- Do they have buttons on their suits?
- What size are their feet?
- How else are they different?

Now color the clowns to make them look different.

Conexión con el hogar

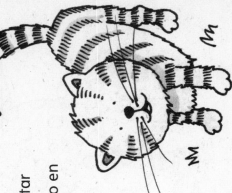

Queridos familiares:

Estoy leyendo *A Tiger Cub Grows Up* esta semana. Estamos repasando cómo comparar y contrastar. Comparo cómo las cosas son parecidas y contrasto cómo son diferentes. En este cuento, estoy leyendo cómo una cachorrita de tigre y un tigre adulto son parecidos y diferentes. Little Tara, la cachorrita de tigre, se pone nerviosa cuando toma su primer baño. En cambio, a los tigres adultos les encanta tirarse al agua y nadar.

Destrezas de la semana

Comprensión: comparar y contrastar

Fonética: sonidos de aw y au como en *pawn* y *pause*

Ortografía: palabras con aw y au

(fold here)

© Macmillan/McGraw-Hill

Nombre _____

Ejercicio de palabras

PALABRAS DE VOCABULARIO

across   air   enough   eyes   learn

cub   wild

Vamos a dibujar Vamos a hacer un dibujo de una oficina del doctor del zoológico, o vamos a pensar en cómo se vería su oficina. Luego, podemos usar las palabras en unas oraciones para describir tu dibujo.

PALABRAS DE ORTOGRAFÍA

cause   claw   dawn

haul   paw   saw

Escríbela correctamente Con tu dedo, escribe cada palabra de ortografía que digo en el aire. Luego deletréalas en voz alta. Después, podemos escribir cada palabra en una hoja de papel.

¡Mira lo que vio Paul!

¡Paul fue al circo! Observa los payasos que vio. Vamos a colorear lo que es parecido acerca de los payasos. Luego, vamos a colorear el resto del dibujo.

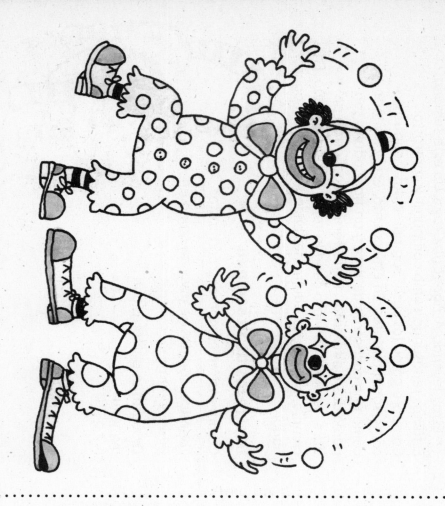

How are these clowns different?

Ahora, vamos a colorear los payasos para que se vean diferentes entre sí. Quizás un payaso tiene gafas. Quizás otro tiene pecas. ¿De qué otras maneras los podemos hacer diferentes?

How are these clowns alike?

Paws for a Cause

by Samuel Pauly

Paws for a Cause

This page is intentionally blank.

If you ever saw a helper dog, you know what it can do. Only some dogs can be trained as helper dogs.

22

This page is intentionally blank.

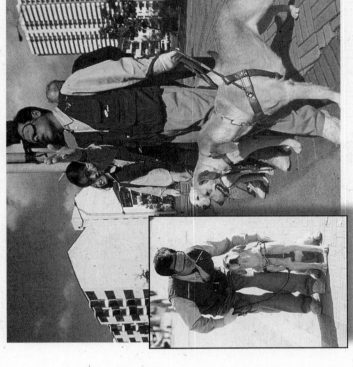

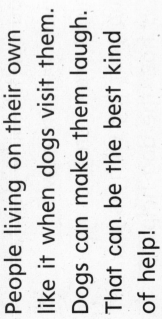

A helper dog goes to school because it needs training. The dog studies to get the helpful skills it will need.

Paws for a Cause

23

People living on their own like it when dogs visit them. Dogs can make them laugh. That can be the best kind of help!

26

If you can't see, a dog can help.
It is trained to pause
for autos in the street.
It hauls things if you can't.

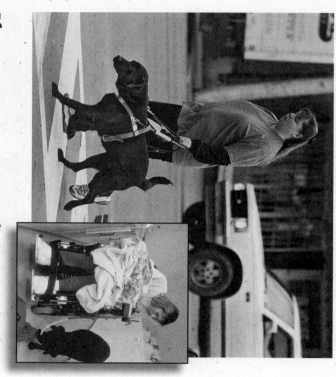

24

If you can't hear, a dog can
tap you with its paw.
It might crawl on your lap
or rub your leg with its jaw.
This is how the dog helps.

25

Watching Horses Grow

by Whitney C. Ryde

Table of Contents

Comprehension Check

Retell

Use a Classify and Categorize Chart to help you compare names given to horses.

Baby	Grownup
1	1
2	2
3	3

Think and Compare

1. How are a horse's eyes like a person's eyes? How are they different?

2. Tell about a horse you have seen. What did it look like?

3. All animals start out as babies and grow. Tell about an animal baby you know about.

16

Chapter 1
How Do Baby Horses Grow?

⊙ This mother horse has a new baby.

Some baby animals are called kids or cubs. A baby horse is called a **foal**. Its mother is called a **mare**. Foals are born in the spring.

Glossary

foal (FOHL) a young horse (page 3)

herd (HURD) a group of animals that live or travel together (page 12)

mare (MAYR) a female horse (page 3)

stallion (STAL-yuhn) an adult male horse (page 14)

Index

Less than an hour after it is born, a foal will stand to drink milk.

A foal's legs grow stronger each day.

Watching Horses Grow

Wild mustangs roam free in the West.

Some horses live in the wild. A male horse, called a **stallion**, leads the herd.

When spring comes, the mares give birth again. The new foals will join the herd.

4

By the time a foal is two weeks old, it can run across a field with the other horses.

⊕ Foals run and play together in a field.

13

Watching Horses Grow

Foals start to eat grass a few weeks after they are born.

 Horses are grazers. They eat grass.

5

Chapter 3

How Do Horses Live Together?

Foals learn to stay in groups with other horses. These groups are called **herds**.

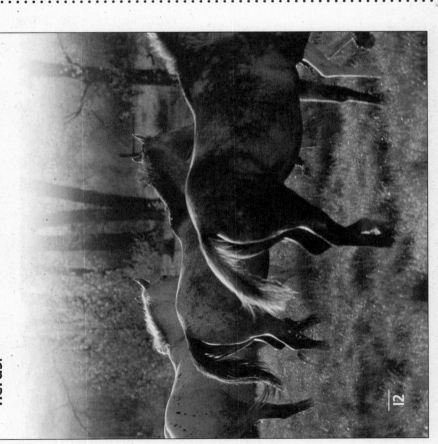

12

You know a foal is a baby horse. Horses have other names as they grow.

What Do You Call a Horse?

Colt
male horse between one and four years old

Stallion
adult male horse

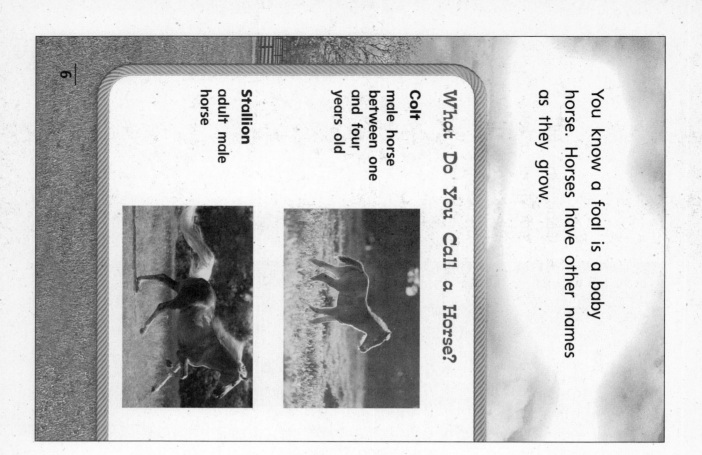

Sometimes horses stand close enough to help each other. One horse can lean across to help clean another horse.

⟳ These two horses are cleaning each other.

Filly
female horse between one and four years old

Mare
adult female horse

◉ This horse is kicking up its rear legs.

Horses have strong legs. They can kick their legs in the air.

Horses have strong tails. Sometimes they flick their tails to shoo away flies and insects.

Chapter 2

What Are the Parts of a Horse?

Horses have very large eyes. They are set on the sides of their heads.

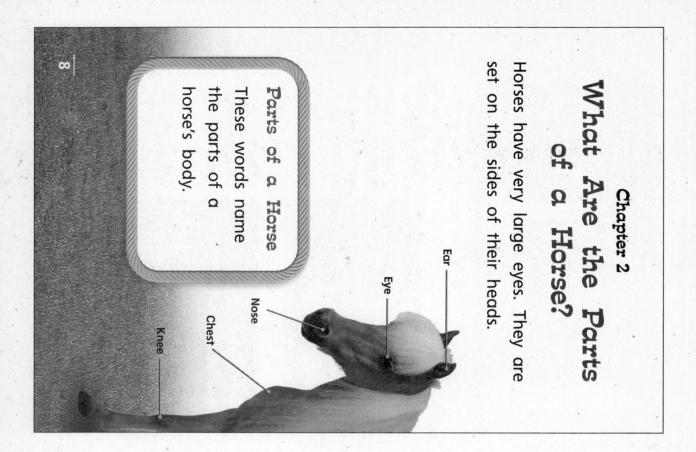

Parts of a Horse

These words name the parts of a horse's body.

Ear
Eye
Nose
Chest
Knee

8

Horses have short pointed ears. They can hear very well. Horses also have a good sense of smell.

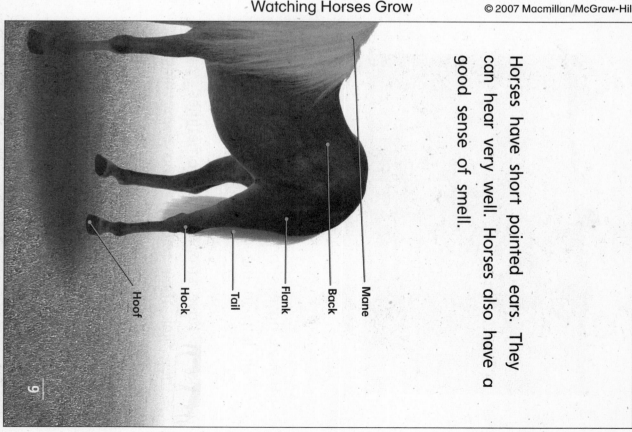

Mane
Back
Flank
Tail
Hock
Hoof

Watching Horses Grow

© 2007 Macmillan/McGraw-Hill

9

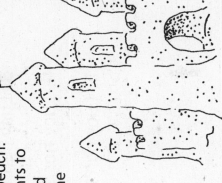

Dear Family Member:

I'm reading *Sand Castle* in class this week. I'm learning about cause and effect. When something happens in a story, it makes something else happen. In this story, Jen is making a sand castle on the beach. A little boy comes by and wants to help. He makes a moat around the castle. Other children come to help. Maybe with even more children, the castle will grow taller and taller!

This Week's Skills

Comprehension: cause and effect

Phonics: sound of oi and oy as in *boil* and *play*

Spelling: words with **oi** and **oy**

(fold here)

© Macmillan/McGraw-Hill

Word Workout

WORDS TO KNOW

circle   toward   grew   leave

toppled   welcoming   wreck

Story Time I'm going to ask you what each word means. Then we can take turns using one of the words in a sentence. We'll listen to each other carefully to build a story with the sentences.

SPELLING WORDS

boy   coin   join

joy   spoil   toy

Sort the Words Let's fold a piece of lined paper in half. Write **oy** and **oi** at the top of each half. Then write your spelling words in the correct list. Can you add words with the same sound to each list?

Name _____

Poor Lucy!

Lucy is having a bad day. Let's read each sentence below and find the cause of her bad luck on the next page. Then write the letter on the line.

___ 1. Lucy is very tired.

___ 2. Lucy didn't eat breakfast.

___ 3. Lucy can't paint her room.

___ 4. Lucy has to give Spot a bath.

___ 5. Lucy can't write her book report.

a. Lucy spilled the can of paint.

b. Lucy didn't sleep well.

c. Lucy didn't read the book.

d. Spot played in the puddle.

e. Lucy burnt the toast.

Conexión con el hogar

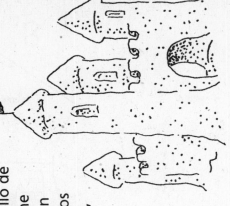

Queridos familiares:

Estoy leyendo *Sand Castle* en la clase esta semana. Estoy aprendiendo sobre las causas y los efectos. Cuando algo ocurre en un cuento, esto hace que ocurra alguna otra cosa. En este cuento, Jen está construyendo un castillo de arena en la playa. Un niño viene y quiere ayudar. Él construye un foso alrededor del castillo. Otros niños vienen a ayudar. ¡Quizás, incluso con más niños, el castillo crecerá más y más!

Destrezas de la semana

Comprensión: causa y efecto

Fonética: los sonidos de *oi* y *oy* como en *boil* y *ploy*

Ortografía: palabras con *oi* y *oy*

(fold here)

© Macmillan/McGraw-Hill

Ejercicio de palabras

PALABRAS DE VOCABULARIO

circle   toward   grew   leave

toppled   welcoming   wreck

Tiempo de cuentos Te voy a preguntar lo que significa cada palabra. Luego, podemos tomar turnos usando una de las palabras en una oración. Vamos a escucharnos con atención para armar juntos un cuento con las oraciones.

PALABRAS DE ORTOGRAFÍA

boy   coin   join

joy   spoil   toy

Ordenar las palabras Vamos a doblar una hoja de papel con renglones a la mitad. Escribe **oy** y **oi** en la parte de arriba de cada mitad. Luego, escribe tus palabras de ortografía en la lista correcta. ¿Puedes agregar palabras con el mismo sonido a cada lista?

Nombre _____

¿Qué va a ocurrir?

Tira una moneda. Mueve un recuadro si sale *heads* y mueve dos recuadros si sale *tails*. Cuando caigas en un dibujo, te ayudaré a leer la causa. Di lo que piensas que va a ocurrir. Vamos a tomar turnos.

GO

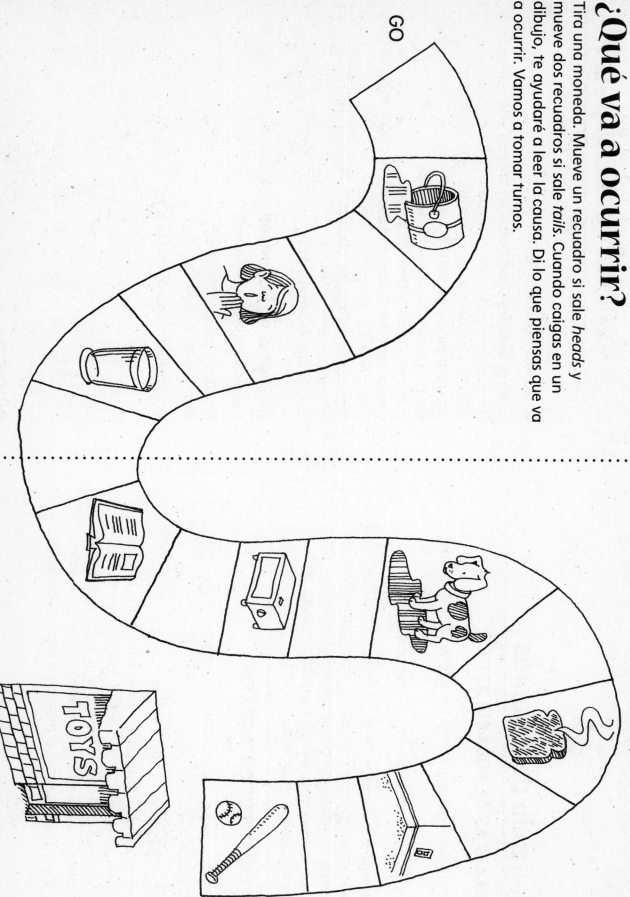

Roy's Rich Soil

by Marsha Boylan
illustrated by Richard Bernal

This page is intentionally blank.

Farmer Roy worked in Illinois.

Roy raised fat hogs.

Roy's hogs made him joyful.

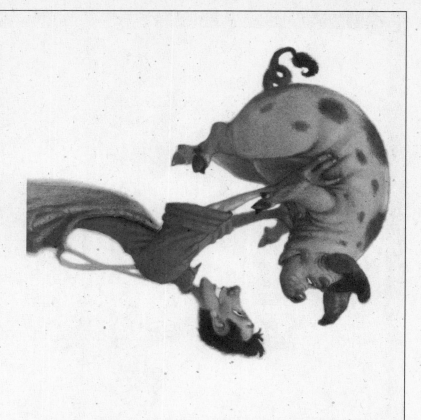

Roy's Rich Soil

This page is intentionally blank.

But Roy did not enjoy one thing.
His hogs OINKED and OINKED!
The noise was enough to keep
Roy up all night!

Roy got rich, thanks to
those noisy hogs.
"Oh, boy! I'm lucky," he said.
"Illinois has some fine soil
for fine corn!"

So Roy sold his hogs to a
farmer across town.
"My farm has rich soil
and fresh air," said Roy.
"I'll learn to raise corn."

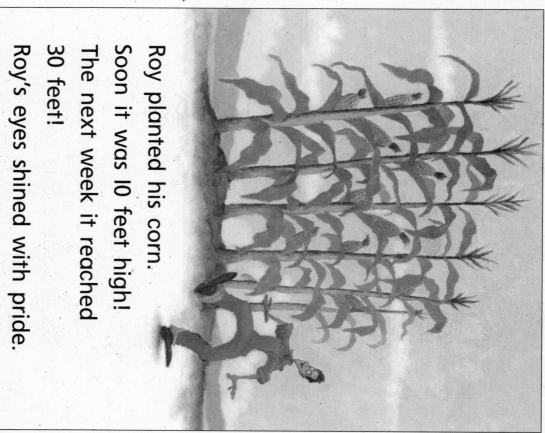

Roy's Rich Soil

Roy planted his corn.
Soon it was 10 feet high!
The next week it reached
30 feet!
Roy's eyes shined with pride.

The Birdhouse

by Sunita Apte

illustrated by Ann Boyajian

Table of Contents

Comprehension Check

Retell the Story

Use a Cause and Effect Chart to tell what happened and why it happened.

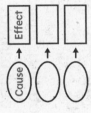

Think and Compare

1. What happened because the children put out the birdhouse?

2. Tell about a time you did not agree with a friend or family member. What happened?

3. Why is putting out a birdhouse helpful to birds?

16

Chapter 1
Let's Make a Birdhouse

Meena looked out at the birds that had come to her backyard.

"Look at how great they are," Meena said. "I want them to stay and not fly away."

2

Suddenly, a family of birds came toward the birdhouse. Some peeked into the house.

"Look, the birds are moving in!" Wendy said.

Meena smiled with joy. She had a birdhouse in her backyard. She hoped the birds would never leave.

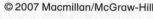

15

"Well, we can make a birdhouse," Mama said. "It would be welcoming and then the birds might not leave."

"That's a great idea," said Meena. "Let's make it this afternoon."

3

The birdhouse looked beautiful when Mama put it in a tree in the backyard.

Meena, Wendy, and Mark sat by the window, looking out toward the birdhouse.

14

Meena called her friends Wendy and Mark to help. Soon Wendy and Mark came over.

"Let's go in here. We can find the things we'll need," said Wendy.

4

Then Mama put the birdhouse together. "The birds are going to love this," she said.

Meena looked at the birdhouse. "Green for the roof was a good choice," she thought. "And so was blue for the walls."

13

So the friends went to work on
their birdhouse. Wendy made
the roof green and put a big circle
of glitter on it. Mark made
the walls blue and added
a red star. Meena covered
the floor with bird stickers.

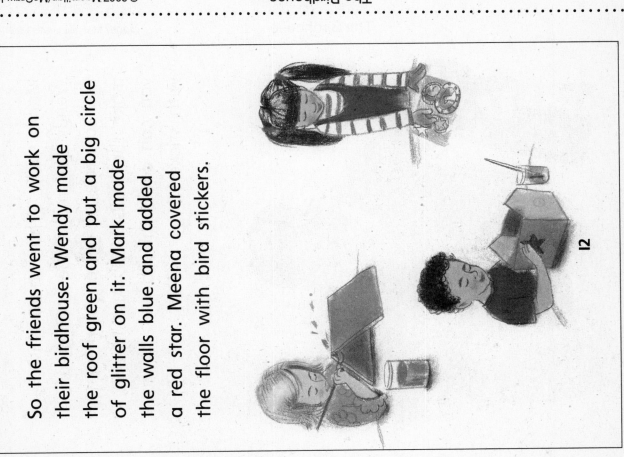

12

The Birdhouse

5

Chapter 2
Getting Ready

Wendy took out paper and paints.
Mark took out wood and glue. And
Meena put out foil stickers.

"Let's make the birdhouse green,
with a circle of glitter," Wendy said.

6

Mama said, "What about this?
Wendy can make the roof green,
with a circle of glitter. Mark can
make the walls blue. And Meena,
you can cover the floor
with stickers."

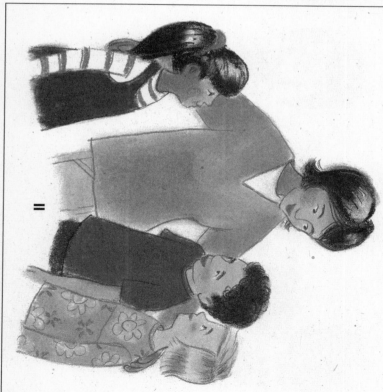

7

"No, let's make the birdhouse blue," Mark said.

"I don't like glitter," said Meena. "I want to use stickers."

7

Chapter 3
Mama Helps

Then Mama came in.

"What's the matter?" she asked.

"We want to make a birdhouse," Meena said. "But we can't agree. Wendy wants it green, with a circle of glitter. Mark wants it blue. And I don't like glitter. I want to use stickers."

Wendy grew upset. "I won't make the birdhouse if it can't be green," she said.

"Well, I won't make it if it isn't blue," Mark said.

8

And by mistake he toppled a jar of red paint.

Meena grew more upset. No one would agree. Would this wreck her plan to make a birdhouse?

9

Calendar

Monday	Tuesday	Wednesday	Thursday	Friday

Name _____

Calendar

© Macmillan/McGraw-Hill

Monday	Tuesday	Wednesday	Thursday	Friday

Name _____

Calendar

Monday	Tuesday	Wednesday	Thursday	Friday

Name _____

481

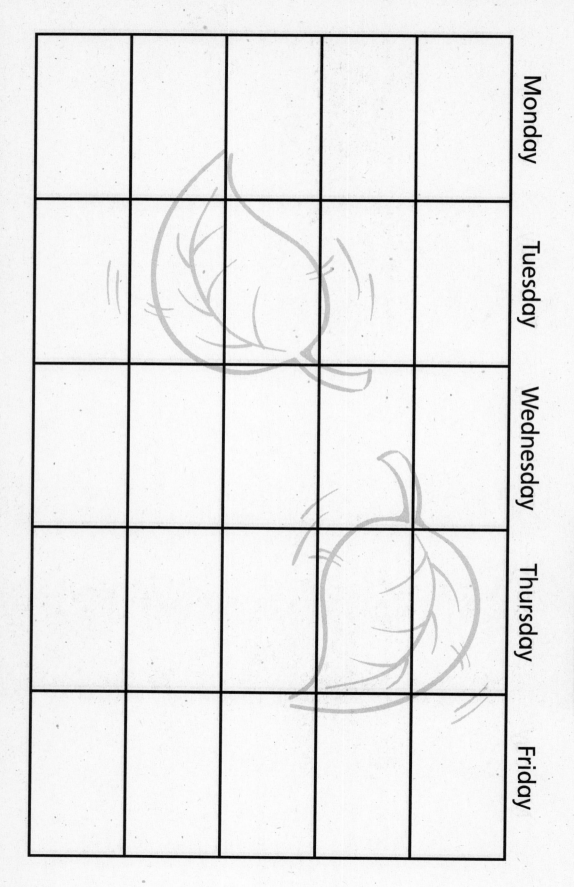

Calendar

Monday	Tuesday	Wednesday	Thursday	Friday

Name _____

Calendar

Monday	Tuesday	Wednesday	Thursday	Friday

Name _____

Calendar

Monday | Tuesday | Wednesday | Thursday | Friday

Name

© Macmillan/McGraw-Hill

484

Calendar

Monday	Tuesday	Wednesday	Thursday	Friday

Name _____

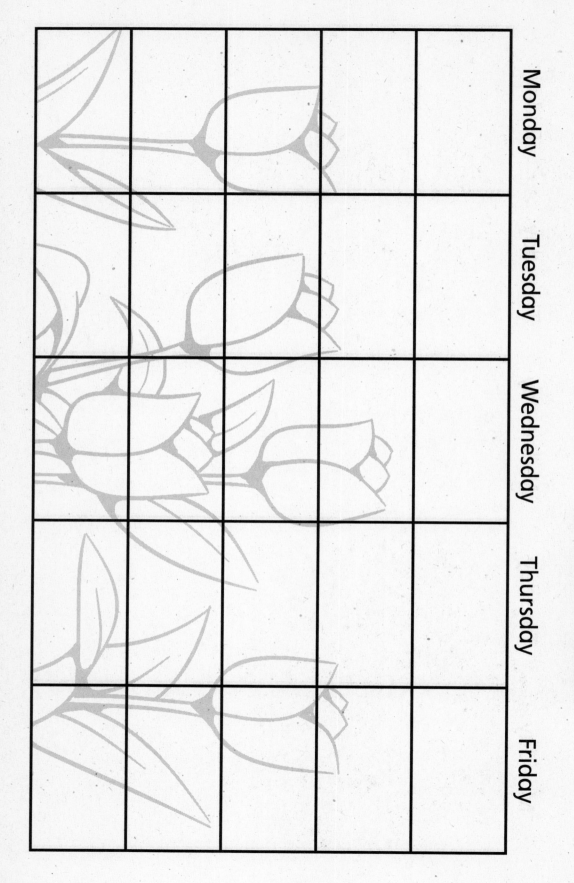

Calendar

Monday	Tuesday	Wednesday	Thursday	Friday

Name _____

Calendar

Monday	Tuesday	Wednesday	Thursday	Friday

Name _____

Calendar

Name ——

Monday	Tuesday	Wednesday	Thursday	Friday

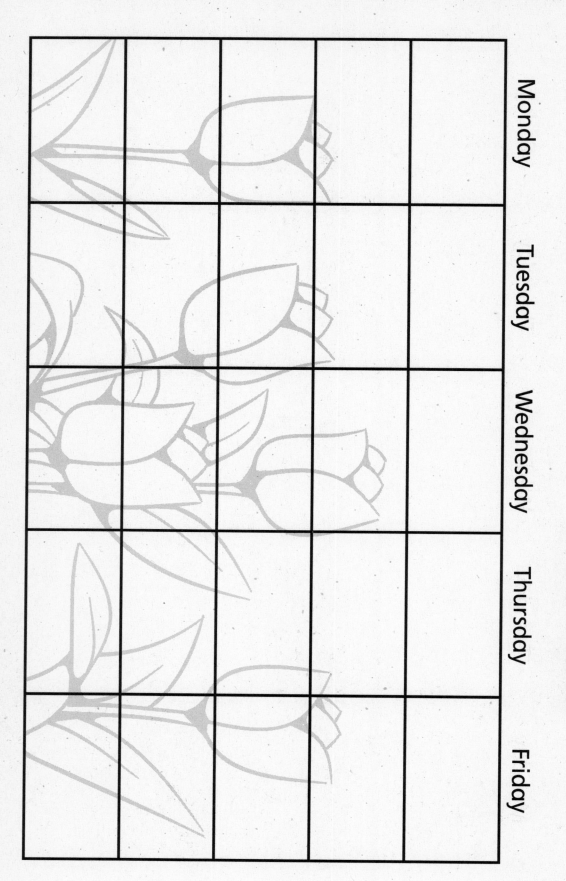

Credits